River Slaney

From Source to Sea

Slaney Bridges and Aspects

Written and Illustrated by
JOHN DUFFY

Foreword by
DICK WARNER

Published by John Duffy,
Tullow, County Carlow, Ireland, 2006
Text © John Duffy 2006
Pencil Drawings © John Duffy 2006

Front Cover: River Slaney at Ouragh, Tullow
Back Cover: Aldborough Bridge

I.S.B.N. 10 digit   0-9554184-0-2
I.S.B.N. 13 digit   978-0-9554184-0-2

Book design by Eoin Duffy,
www.shabadahay.com

Book printed by
Grafton Litho Ltd, 19 Hanover St., Dublin 2

Pencil drawings scanned by
Master Photo Ltd., 4 Heytesbury Lane,
Ballsbridge, Dublin 4

An Tsláine

Ó Fhoinse go Farraige

BOOK SPONSORS

This publication has been assisted by the financial support of

Gillespie's SuperValu, Mill St., Baltinglass, County Wicklow

Hickson's SuperValu, Bridge St., Tullow, County Carlow

Caulfield's SuperValu, Abbey Square, Enniscorthy, County Wexford

GILLESPIE'S SUPERVALU, Baltinglass

The local jail in the rebellion year of 1798 was situated beside the bridge at Mill St., Baltinglass. Rebels from west Wicklow were held here, and many were executed. Today, the site contains a SuperValu supermarket, owned by Arthur Gillespie.

In the early 1900s, Webb's grocery and hardware business operated here. This business was purchased by Hugh P. Doyle who continued to trade under the Webb name. In 1940, the business was purchased by Arthur Gillespie's father, Norman Gillespie of Carlow, for £2,200. Norman Gillespie continued to trade under the Webb name into the 1950s.

The premises was extended in 1962, when it became a supermarket and hardware shop. In 1971, Arthur Gillespie took over the management of the business. In 1972, the Hollow Bar next door was purchased. This building was demolished and developed into Gillespie's Hardware, which conducted business until the end of 1999. In 2000, Arthur Gillespie opened his present supermarket.

Gillespie's have operated under the SuperValu logo since 1985. The old building, which has been restored to its original condition, now accommodates a coffee shop and an office supplies business.

Baltinglass, a rural market town, has served the people of west Wicklow for many generations and Gillespie's look forward to continuing this tradition into the future.

Baltinglass viewed from
Webb's grocery

HICKSON'S SUPERVALU, Tullow

Andy Byrne, a native of Drumphea, spent his early years in the grocery business in Bagenalstown and Carlow. In 1933, he married Kathleen Harney. Also that year, he purchased Halligan's grocery business in Tullow. Halligan's were renowned for the quality of their bacon and Andy Byrne continued this tradition. The original shop was 400 sq. ft.

Mrs. Kathleen Byrne did not work directly in the shop but she was kept busy rearing seven children. Also, at that time, staff tended to live with their employer.

Customers, in the early days, were mostly farmers. They bought groceries, mealstuff and some hardware. Byrnes also purchased produce from their farming customers, such as butter and eggs.

Andy Byrne's son, Paddy, began work in the shop in 1953, direct from school and he took over the family business in the late 1960s. The business continued to prosper and a number of extensions were carried out. In 1994, Byrne's garage was incorporated into the supermarket and car park.

In 2003, Byrne's supermarket was purchased by Tommy and Bridgy Hickson. A native of Bennekerry, County Carlow, Tommy Hickson previously worked in the retail trade with SuperValu and L & N for 18 years. The shop has been a SuperValu supermarket since 2003. In 2006, on ground purchased at the rear of the shop, Hickson's built an extension which doubled the shop floor area to 12,000 sq. ft. This extension included the incorporation of Tullow's new Post Office into the business.

Bridge St., Tullow

CAULFIELD'S SUPERVALU, Enniscorthy
In 1575, the Franciscans had an abbey here.

In the Portsmouth Estate Records, entries refer to lease agreements on this site such as one, in 1859, concerning 'a tenement called the Salt Store now used as a sawmills'. In 1878, a steam sawmill opened here, under the name of T. Smith & Sons. A later occupier of the property, William Fortune, a building contractor, operated here before the property came under the control of Wexford County Council. Enniscorthy Agricultural Co-Operative Society was formed in response to the pioneering work in the formation of co-operatives in Ireland by Sir Horace Plunkett (1854-1932). Early members of the Society in Enniscorthy were Mr. Harold Lett and his wife, Annette Edith. Mrs. Lett was the founder of the Irish Countrywomen's Association. The Co-Op store in Enniscorthy served the community for many years selling hardware, iron, coal and agricultural implements.

In 1916, the Co-Op Garage moved from the yard at Abbey Quay and began operating from the old cinema premises at Abbey Square. The Enniscorthy Motor Company was established in 1918 and, in 1925, it won a prestigious Ford dealership.

Today, the SuperValu store at Abbey Square is owned by the Caulfield / McCarthy Group and trades as Caulfield's SuperValu. The shop, which is 20,000 sq. ft. in area, opened in the early 1990s and was owned by the L & N group who sold it to Musgraves in 1995. Caulfields acquired the store in 1997.

The other locations for stores within the Caulfield / McCarthy group are New Ross, Kilkenny, Waterford, Tipperary, Malahide, Bandon, and Merchants' Quay in Cork city.

Abbey Square,
Enniscorthy ,1896

Contents

ACKNOWLEDGEMENTS

A special word of thanks to Dick Warner for writing the foreword and to Dr. Ron Cox for providing engineering information on Slaney bridges.

DICK WARNER
Dick Warner is a writer by profession who works in print, radio and television. His print work includes writing for the Examiner newspaper. He is best known for his television series, *Waterways*, a series of water journeys around Ireland examining the environment from many different perspectives. He was born in 1946 and graduated from Trinity College, Dublin. He is married with two children and lives on an organic small holding in rural County Kildare.

DR. RONALD COX
Dr. Ronald Cox is an engineering historian and Director of the Centre for Civil Engineering Heritage at Trinity College, Dublin, which he founded in 1995. He has published widely in the fields of civil engineering heritage and engineering biography. He is a member of the Heritage Society of Engineers Ireland and of the Industrial Heritage Association of Ireland. He is a long-serving member of the Panel for Historical Engineering Works (PHEW) of the Institution of Civil Engineers.

'Dr. Cox's assistance in the production of this book is much appreciated. On visits to Trinity College, Dublin, he expertly looked over my photographs of bridges, seeing things that often escaped my eye. He explained masonry styles, arch design and clues to the age of a bridge. The engineering information he supplied on Slaney bridges enhances this book and he also supplied biographical information on the County Surveyors who built Slaney bridges in the 1800s'. – J.D.

Further assistance with this project was gratefully received from the following:

Robert Butler (Wicklow County Library)
John Callanan (Engineers Ireland)
David Carbery (Enniscorthy Museum)
Deirdre Condron (Carlow County Library)
Peader and Kathleen Cullen, Rathdangan
An tAthair Séamus de Val, Bunclody
Carmel Flahavan (Carlow County Library)
Christine Flood (Wicklow County Council)
Sergeant Ger Fogarty (Irish Defence Forces)
Commandant Derek Hanly (Irish Defence Forces)
Paddy Hatton (Slaney Branch, Inland Waterways Association of Ireland)
Martin Kelly (Eastern Regional Fisheries Board)
Veronica McCallion (Central Bank Currency Services, Dublin)
Dr. Conchubhar Ó Crualaoich (Placenames Branch, Dept. of Community, Rural and Gaeltacht Affairs, Dublin)
Jimmy O'Toole, Carlow
Celestine Rafferty (Wexford County Library Service)

Location maps, courtesy Barry Dalby, EastWest Mapping, Clonegal.
Photo of boating on the Slaney, p.104, courtesy Paddy Hatton, Slaney branch IWAI
Photo of the source of River Slaney, p. 18, courtesy Martin Kelly, ERFB.
Photos of British Army in Glen of Imaal, p.22, p.25, courtesy Commandant Derek Hanly, Coolmoney Camp, Glen of Imaal.
Photo of the building of Rathdrum viaduct, p.35, courtesy Engineers Ireland archives.
Masons' tools, p.29, from Mitchell, Charles F., Building Construction and Drawing, London, 1900.
Irish £20 bank note, p.118, courtesy Currency Services, Central Bank & Financial Services Authority of Ireland, Dublin.

The woodcuts used in this book are by Thomas Bewick (1753-1828), of Northumberland, England. He was a unique artist who portrayed rural life with skill and a sense of humour.

To Ann,
Simon, Eoin, Emmet and Ciarán

ABOUT THIS PROJECT

This book began as an 'art' idea. I had planned to produce prints of bridge drawings but, in a short time, I realised there was a larger project emerging. I initially did not realise there were so many bridges on the River Slaney, especially in County Wicklow. (There are 12 bridges above Baltinglass, over one third of the river's total). I read accounts such as the Ordnance Field Books of 1839 and Samuel Lewis' travels in the 1830s. Local history stories began to accumulate and I knew that, put together, they would make an interesting book, united by the common theme of the River Slaney flowing through them. The addition of further 'river essays' on Angling, Boating, etc., compliment the book's theme of Slaney Bridges. Each bridge was visited several times with my camera. Most photographs were taken in Spring 2005. Some overgrown bridges had to wait until the following winter to be photographed. (Wicklow, the 'Garden of Ireland', lived up to its name in this regard). The subsequent pencil drawings took over

six months to complete. History information came from several sources- libraries, museums, individuals and various bodies such as the Eastern Regional Fisheries Board and the Inland Waterways Association of Ireland. The Internet was particularly useful. Book sources are listed in the Bibliography.

TO THE ART-MINDED

All bridges were drawn in pencil from my own photographs and some drawings took over forty hours to complete. Composition of scene depended on one main photograph which viewed the subject from an artistic point of view as well as an architectural one. Some bridges looked best in the evening while others were photographed in early morning light. Paper used was 250gm. extra-smooth Bristol Board Paper, A3 in size. This paper, being both smooth and tough, is suitable for multiple layers of pencil. I use two types of pencil. Derwent Pencils, the original graphite product from Cumbria, impart lovely tone. They can be a little 'gritty' but this adds to certain surface appearances, such as stonework. For extra-smooth finish, such as depicting a calm river pool, I use Faber Castell's varnish pencil. This 'man-made' pencil is highly consistant and gives a unique smoothness. Pencil grades used were 4B, 2B, B, 2H and 4H. I make much use of rubbers. Cut into pieces of varying angles, they can impart dramatic effects. Brand does not appear to matter, but one rubber type is unique. A pencil colleague, Mike Sibley in Yorkshire, discovered the use of Blu-tac as a pencil rubber. This material, when touched to a drawing, lifts pencil-work gently off the page, creating unusual effects. I am self-taught, having learned techniques by accident as much as any other method. My ability increased rapidly in recent years after I got the Internet, and is still improving. Through the Internet, the best pencil artists in the world enter my sitting room and freely impart their techniques to me. – J.D.

THE WRITER / ARTIST

Originally from Hacketstown, County Carlow, John Duffy attended school in Hacketstown N.S. and Newbridge College, where he sat his Leaving Cert.

A self-taught artist, he draws portrait commissions of people, homes and pets. His interest in local history enables him to combine research with his artistic talent. His previous book, *Churches of Kildare and Leighlin*, won an Illustrator's Award in 2002. He has lived since 1984 at Tullow, County Carlow and, having reared four sons with his wife, Ann, they now live in a quiet house with their boxer, Sasha. His hobbies are fly fishing and playing traditional Irish music.

FOREWORD BY DICK WARNER

Unless I'm in a great hurry, or unless the weather is foul, when I drive up to a bridge over a river I look for a place to park. I love hanging over parapets and watching rivers. I've always been that way. I love fishing in rivers, boating on rivers and watching river birds. But I'm also quite content just looking at a river. I look at eddies and swirls that might be trout lies. I watch tresses of ranunculus weed waving in the current like green mermaid's hair. I try and spot hatches of water insects. I can easily spend an hour or two at a good bridge over a good river. A good bridge is a fairly low one, so that you're not too far from the surface of the water. It should have a parapet that's a comfortable height for leaning on and, preferably, 'pedestrian refuges' so you don't get run over by a tractor. And a good river? Well, that's a little more difficult to define. All rivers are different and they all have something to offer. But probably the best rivers to watch are fairly fast flowing and have stones and boulders in them. Interesting vegetation on the banks is an advantage, but the main thing is that the water should weave through channels between obstructions, constantly changing speed and direction. Islands and islets are a real bonus.

All of this makes the Slaney a particularly fascinating river. From its source as a little mountain stream high up in the Glen of Imaal down to where it meets the tide in Enniscorthy it is, for the most part, a fast-flowing, stony river. Its estuary offers very different attractions --- but there are bridges worth hanging over down there as well. I have met other people who share my passion for watching rivers but I accept that it's a bit of a minority pastime. But perhaps this will change now that we have such an excellent guide to one of the most watchable rivers in Ireland. John's book not only illustrates every single bridge over the Slaney, it also includes a huge amount of information about the river in general and the bridges in particular.

So if you're something of a beginner when it comes to river watching you now have an ideal tool. You can look at the drawings and evaluate the potential of the parapet as a viewing platform. You can read the text and, however well you know the area, you're guaranteed that you'll find fascinating new information. And when it finally gets dark you can open the book again in the privacy of your own home and do some vicarious river watching. I love this book. I'll use it and I'll enjoy it. Perhaps in the second edition John could include suggestions about good places for me to park near the bridges. Then I could spend a month or two hanging over each one of them.

Chapter 1

The River Slaney

Source of the River Slaney at Lugnaquillia, County Wicklow

THE RIVER SLANEY

The River Slaney derives its name from Sláinghe, a King of the Fir Bolg, an ancient race that came to Ireland and divided Ireland into five provinces. These provinces were governed by five brothers. *'Sláinghe, the eldest brother, had the Province of Leynster for his part, which containeth Inver Colpe (Drogheda) to the meeting of the three waters, by Waterford, where the three rivers, Suyre, Ffeoir and Barrow do meet and run together into the sea'.* He lived at his fort, Dinn Rí, on the River Barrow between Carlow and Leighlin and the town of Slane in County Meath is also called after him.

The River Slaney begins at a point called North Prison at Lugnaquillia Mountain in County Wicklow, at an elevation of over 3,000 ft. The young river winds its way through the Glen of Imaal where it is joined by the Leoh, Knickeen and Little Slaney rivers. The Slaney's larger tributaries are the Derreen, the Derry, the Clody, the Bann, the Urrin and the Boro.

About 15 miles from its source, (and 13 bridges later), the Slaney flows through the town of Baltinglass, County Wicklow. A short distance south of Baltinglass, at an elevation of 400 ft., the Slaney leaves County Wicklow and flows through east County Carlow, passing through Rathvilly and Tullow. From Kildavin bridge, the Slaney leaves County Carlow and commences its leisurely journey through the rich farmlands of County Wexford, passing through Bunclody, Clohamon and Enniscorthy. The Slaney is tidal for 13 miles from Enniscorthy and it joins the sea at the town of Wexford.

The River Slaney has varied and plentiful wildlife. Herds of deer can be seen in Wicklow and along the river one may see swans, dippers, wild ducks and herons. The kingfisher can be seen darting by and, at dusk, one may see bats, owls and otters. The mudflats at Wexford harbour are favoured by black-headed gulls, redshanks, oystercatchers and nearby are the famous Slobs, wintering grounds of migratory birds.

Wild brown trout are numerous. Salmon and sea trout return annually to spawn in the river but stocks of Atlantic Salmon are

Mouth of the River Slaney
at Wexford

only a shadow of former years with blame being placed on several factors.

The River Slaney is regarded as one of the fastest-flowing rivers in Europe but the volume of water in the river appears to be less than in times gone by. Accounts written about the river in the 1830s refer, typically, to bridges of four or five arches with 'water flowing through all arches', whereas today, three arches may well suffice. With much land drainage conducted over the years, water run-off is now fast and when floods occur, they are high and brief. Flood relief works have been conducted in some towns and more are proposed. Demand for water to supply new housing schemes is also high as the population in the region increases. This puts pressure on the river, especially in Summer and this situation is not helped by inadequate sewage threatment facilities along the river.

The E.U. has appointed Special Areas of Conservation (SACs) across Europe and the River Slaney is included in the ap-prox.10,000 sq. km. identified in Ireland. The 25 Irish species that must be afforded protection include such 'Slaney' species as the salmon, otter and freshwater mussel.

The E.U. introduced the Water Framework Directive in December 2000 to plan the management and quality of water supply in conjunction with the protection of aquatic ecosystems. Ireland has eight designated regions, and the River Slaney is in the South Eastern River Basin District.

'Rivers and the inhabitants of the watery elements are made for
wise men to contemplate and for fools to pass by without consideration'.

Izaak Walton, *The Compleat Angler*, (1653)

THE GLEN OF IMAAL
Source of the River Slaney

The Glen is named from a tribe known as *Uí Máil*, who once occupied the area. *Mál* was brother of Cathair Mór, King of Ireland in the 2nd century.

The landscape of County Wicklow is dominated by an expanse of granite that runs through the County, dividing the east coast from the lowlands of west Wicklow. The glaciated valleys of Glendalough and Glenmalure contrast with the rolling glens of west Wicklow. Of these broad glens, Imaal in the southwest of the county is the largest, being 6 miles long and 4.5 miles wide. At its eastern end is Lugnaquillia, the highest mountain in County Wicklow.

The earliest human settlements in County Wicklow date between.4000-2500 B.C. Several burial sites survive from this period, such as at Baltinglass Hill. Raths, or ring forts, are numerous throughout the County and these were the homes of the aristocracy. There are also many stone circles and sites of interest in the Glen area such as at Donard and Castleruddery.

County Wicklow glens were home to 'saints & scholars' and the magnificent monastic site at Glendalough attracts thousands of visitors each year. In 431, Saint Palladius founded a church near Donard and, in 432, Saint Patrick founded one at Donoughmore.

The River Slaney flows for over 70 miles from Lugnaquillia's northern slopes to the sea at Wexford. As a small river, it travels through the Glen of Imaal and is joined by the tributaries, Leoh, Knickeen and Little Slaney rivers. From Lugnaquillia's southern side, the river Derreen, one of the Slaney's main tributaries, rises. It joins the River Slaney below Tullow, in County Carlow.

Wicklow was the last county to be incorporated, in 1606. Before then, Baltinglass was in County Kildare, Arklow was in County Wexford and Wicklow town was in County Dublin.

In the 13th century, Government papers described the rich farmlands of Dublin, Kildare and Carlow as 'terra pacis', land of peace, and the highlands of Wicklow as 'terra guerre', land of war. Expelled from their lands in Kildare, the O'Tooles and O'Byrnes settled in the mountains of Wicklow from where they waged war on the Government.

Turmoil continued in the Glen with the outbreak of the 1798 Rebellion. Rebels in west Wicklow were led by Michael Dwyer of Imaal and, reminiscent of Wicklow in the middle ages, Dwyer and his followers continued to harass the Government for five years after the rebellion ended, until his surrender in December, 1803.

In the 1830s, the population of the Glen was over 4,000 people, engaged mainly in farming. This figure halved during the Famine of the 1840s.

THE IRISH DEFENCE FORCES
Leitrim Barracks, near Seskin bridge in the Glen of Imaal, was one of five barracks constructed through County Wicklow after the rebellion of 1798. It was designed to house 200 troops but was never used, as more peaceful times followed. It is now in ruins.

Inscription with photograph: 47th Fd Arty Bde Permnt Huts Moodys Farm Cannow, Lugnaquilla, & Camara, Glen of Imaal, Co. Wicklow, '05

Inscription with photograph: "141st Bty ROYAL FIELD ARTILLERY" in action behind cover Artillery Practice Camp, Glen of Imaal, Co. Wicklow, July '07

In the 1890s, the British Army decided to use the upper Glen area as an artillery range, it being an ideal expanse, surrounded by mountains and situated near the Curragh Camp in County Kildare. In the following years, 22 families (126 people) in this area were forced to leave their holdings. Owners of land were compensated but 6 families were 'tenants at will' and may not have received anything.

After Independence in 1922, the camp was used during summer months by Irish troops, who used to fire at targets on the mountain slopes, left by the British.

The Department of Defence owns approximately 8,000 acres in the Glen of Imaal today with headquarters at Coolmoney Camp. The area continues to be used as an artillery training range and is the only such one in the State. Both Irish and overseas troops are trained here, in preparation for peace-keeping duties abroad, with the U.N.

The Glen of Imaal is rich in wildlife and the headwaters of the River Slaney are within the Army artillery range. These are the spawning grounds for Atlantic salmon. Poaching occurs each autumn when the fish return from the sea. The Defence Forces are engaged in protecting these areas, assisting officers of the Fisheries Board, and they have built a special watchtower to look out for poachers along the river.

The Defence Forces are also engaged in conservation work and have placed tons of gravel and stone in streams to improve salmon spawning beds.

Hill walking is very popular in the Glen area and the 'Lug' Marathon Walk and Ring of Imaal Walk take place on alternate years.

The Artillery Range has a perimeter of 20 miles and the locality is also popular with hill walkers. Accidents have occurred over the years when people happened on unexploded shells, including one fatal accident in 1979. The Department of Defence has an Army Information & Advice Centre at old Seskin school, where visitors are advised of safe walking routes and given maps of the area.

THE METAL BRIDGE
A small crossing on the River Slaney, this bridge is situated in a restricted area within the artillery range of the Irish Defence Forces. It is in the townland of Cannow, (*Ceann Abha*, head of the river), and is built of steel girders and concrete. It is only 5 feet wide and bears the inscription '2nd Fld Engineers 22/6/88'. It replaced an earlier bridge.

Chapter 2

Bridges

THE BUILDING OF ROAD BRIDGES IN IRELAND

In ancient times, the shallow crossing points of rivers were crucial for travel and communication. These fords were in use before the construction of bridges and the country's main routes were determined by their locations. Towns grew at such points and bear testimony to their past in their present-day names, such as Athlone (*Áth Luain*, the ford of *Luain*, a man's name) and Athy (*Áth I*, after the killing there of a Munster chief, *Ae*).

Bridges were later built at these crossings and *droichead*, the Irish word for bridge, is very ancient. The 14th Abbot of Iona, from 726 to 752 A.D., was Cilline, known as *Droichteach*, the bridge maker.

Over time, river crossings became both military strategic points and centres of commerce throughout Ireland.

As the first stone bridges were being built on the Thames, King John ordered that stone bridges be built across the Shannon at Limerick and across the Liffey at Dublin. Today, there are about 25,000 bridges in Ireland possessing a span of 6ft. or more.

The bridges we have today are generally not ancient. Early bridges, built of wood, required constant repair and were often swept away in floods, as were early stone bridges. The earliest recorded bridge in Ireland is the remains of a timber bridge at Clonmacnoise in County Offaly, which crossed the River Shannon. It was discovered in 1994 and has been carbon-dated at 804 A.D.

Bridges with stone arches began to be built in Ireland after the arrival of the Religious Orders and the Normans in the 12th century. Both groups had highly-skilled stone masons, as their legacy of monasteries and castles testify.

The Statute Labour System was brought to Ireland under the Highway Act (1613-15). Every year, under this law, parishes elected a Surveyor and Orderer. Six days were determined at Easter for repair of parish roads. Every farmer had to supply two men and tools to work for eight hours. Also, 'Every householder and every cottier (hired servants excepted) shall each day go or send a labourer on pain of 2s. per day for default'.

Local Grand Juries were established in 1710. These bodies consisted mainly of wealthy landowners selected by the County Sheriff. They met twice yearly to assess proposed public works and rates were levied to pay for building schemes. Many of the Grand Jury records were lost when the Public Records Office in the Four Courts in Dublin was burned down in 1921.

The first Turnpike Act (1727) allowed for the collection of tolls on specified lengths of road. This Act stated a minimum road width of 12ft. A later Act increased this to 14ft. and as the Act included bridges, many old crossings were re-built, which partly explains the small number of very old bridges surviving today. Tolls were charged at major bridges and bridge keepers were often appointed.

A remarkable engineer arrived on the scene in the late 1700s. Lemuel Cox, an American, had become famous in the United States for building long wooden bridges across gorges and big rivers as the West was

'Cities grew up around them and castles were built to command them. Battles were fought for their possession. History– social, economic and military- clusters more thickly about bridges than about towns and citadels'. John Buchan, in De la Mare (1975).

opened up. John Harvey, Bishop of Derry, persuaded Derry Corporation to invite the American to build a bridge across the River Foyle. Work began in 1789 and the bridge, 1,068ft. long and 40ft. wide, opened in 1791. Cox brought all his equipment and materials in ships from America and worked with a team of 24 American tradesmen. The timber used was Quebec Oak, often in lengths of 80ft. He built six further wooden bridges in Ireland – Waterford, New Ross, Mountgarret, Portumna, Ferrycarrig and Wexford.

The Irish Board of Public Works was appointed in 1831. This body greatly contributed to road construction and in 1834, a Surveyor was appointed to each county. In 1898, power was transferred to local County Councils who, assisted by Urban Councils, took over the function of the Grand Juries. In 1909, taxes were imposed on motorists and money raised went into a Road Fund for road improvements. The fund was inadequate and road quality was poor. Following the Treaty of 1922, the Irish Government had the task of repairing bridges blown up in the Civil War. Up to the time of World War Two, 365 bridges were improved or replaced and 112 new ones built.

In the 1960s, over 1,500 miles of road were designated for development as the country's principal routes. Modern engineering, using concrete and steel, enabled the crossing of rivers in flat spans.

Arterial drainage schemes were enacted for local flood relief. Over 6,000 bridges were affected by work on 2,000 miles of river channel and many bridges had to be strengthened or replaced.

Today, Ireland's bridges on regional roads are the responsibility of Local Authorities under the Department of the Environment, Heritage & Local Government. Primary road bridges are the responsibility of the National Roads Authority (NRA).

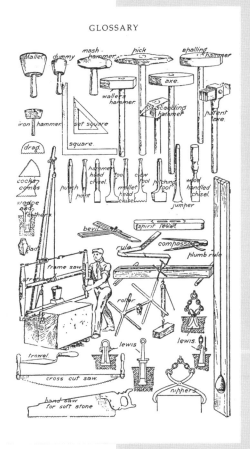

GLOSSARY

Masons' Tools, from Mitchell, Charles F., "Building Construction and Drawing", London, 1900

BRIDGES OF THE RIVER SLANEY

Early crossings on Irish rivers were often destroyed in floods. Severe winters occurred in the 1800s which destroyed many bridges – the bridge at New Ross, for example, was swept away by ice in 1867.

As elsewhere in Ireland, Slaney bridges are not very old. In the Down Survey of 1656, Clonegal (Kilcarry) is shown as the only bridge across the Slaney or any other river in county Wexford at that time.

Today, there are 32 road bridges and one railway bridge along the Slaney. There are 14 bridges in County Wicklow, 7 in County Carlow and 12 in County Wexford (including the railway crossing at Enniscorthy).

Slaney bridges were built at highest density in the Wicklow mountains. From the Glen of Imaal to Baltinglass, there are 13 bridges along 13 miles while in the flatlands of County Wexford, there are 11 road bridges along 32 miles.

About one third of Slaney bridges date from, or before, 1800. These are often narrow structures on minor roads that escaped the road-widening laws of the 18th century. They are distinguished by their stonework and features such as arches of varying profile and cutwaters that often rise to parapet level, examples being Ballyhubbock (County Wicklow) and Ballycarney (County Wexford).

A high standard of construction was performed by stonemasons in the 1800s and a Surveyor was appointed to each county following an Act of Parliament in 1834.

Most masonry bridges along the Slaney in County Wicklow are of standard 3-arch design and there are also the two impressive single-arch bridges of *George's* and *Waterloo* that display fine workmanship. (With spans of 40ft and 48ft respectively, these are the biggest single-span masonry bridges on the River Slaney.)

After leaving County Wicklow, the River Slaney widens and the first crossing in County Carlow is the 6-arch bridge at Rathvilly. County Carlow also contains two rare Slaney bridge types at Moatabower and Tullow, which were built in the 1840s.

These are faced entirely with cut granite, the fine stonework extending from the arches up to the parapet walls. Their flattened masonry arches, (the only such on the Slaney), were designed to minimise gradient and they display high engineering skill.

In County Wexford, Moll's map of 1714 indicates ferries operating at Scarawalsh and Wexford and, up to 1795, there were no bridges on the River Slaney below the town of Enniscorthy.

Bridges of American oak were constructed at Ferrycarrig and Wexford by the American engineer, Lemuel Cox, in the 1790s. Wexford wooden bridge, at 1,554ft., was the longest Slaney bridge ever built and cost £15,000. It had Chinese railings, seating areas and recesses for two orchestras. This bridge was the scene of murder and execution a few years later, in the rebellion of 1798.

County Wexford contains the biggest variety of bridge types on the river. Enniscorthy possesses the Slaney's only railway bridge.

The town also has one of the river's oldest bridges (1775) as well as a new bridge addition (Seamus Rafter bridge, 1991).

Ballycarney (c.1780) is the only Slaney bridge where raised cutwaters provide stand-in 'pedestrian refuges' and is also unique in displaying protruding stones in the pillars which were used to support timbers during construction of its arches.

Scarawalsh bridge (1790) is an excellent example of a late eighteenth century bridge, built to a generous width of 21ft and never widened or altered over the years.

The 1915 concrete bridge at Killurin has a lifting section that once facilitated river traffic and there is an unusual single-lane concrete bridge at Edermine (1975).

County Wexford also contains the modern bridges of Scarawalsh, Ferrycarrig and the award-winning bridge at Wexford town which, at 383m., is the longest (and most recent) bridge on the Slaney.

The foundations of old Slaney bridges have received modern-day protection from the scouring action of water. The usual remedy is to pave the river bed with concrete and to place concrete 'skirts' around the base of pillars. This work, unfortunately, is conducted with little regard for bridge aesthetics.

Modern bridges bear plaques informing us about 'the builder', 'date built' and who performed the opening ceremony. Of all the old Slaney bridges, only four bear such information. They are Seskin, Gibstown, Eldon and Aldborough, all of which are in County Wicklow.

Aldborough Bridge

THE BUILDERS OF SLANEY BRIDGES

With the formation of Landed Estates in the 1600s, a sense of order emerged relating to construction projects. This applied to the building of gentry houses, town layouts and the construction of roads, including bridges.

In 1710, Grand Juries were formed in each county to assess proposed public works and levy rates to pay for them. Grand Juries were comprised of landlords and the body was headed by the County Sheriff. The Grand Juries conducted the building of new bridges and the widening of old ones, (such as at Enniscorthy and Bunclody). Grand Juries were in charge of building projects until the formation of County Councils in 1898.

The American engineer, Lemuel Cox, built two bridges of American oak across the River Slaney in the 1790s, at Ferrycarrig and Wexford. These were the first bridges on the river built below Enniscorthy.

The appointment of a Surveyor to each county after 1834 raised standards of construction. Henry Brett was appointed Surveyor for County Wicklow in 1853. Charles G. Forth became Surveyor for County Carlow in 1834 and in 1840, James Barry Farrell was appointed Surveyor for County Wexford.

These men were engaged in various engineering projects in the southeast ranging from town water schemes to building railway lines and they also built bridges over several rivers, including the Slaney.

In recent times, bridges have been built by County Councils. These bridges are flat beam structures that replaced damaged older bridges such as at Stratford-on Slaney in County Wicklow, or bypassed others, such as at Scarawalsh in County Wexford.

Killurin Bridge, with lifting section, was built by the British Reinforced Concrete Engineering Company in 1915. Another concrete bridge was built in 1975 at Edermine, by IrishEngCo.

The new Scarawalsh bridge (opened 1976) was designed by McCarthy & Partners under the supervision of Professor Swako of Liverpool University. The contractors were Public Works Limited. The structural engineer, Peter Sheehy, later went on to design the concrete bridges at Enniscorthy, Ferrycarrig and Wexford for John B.Barry & Partners.

The new bridge at Enniscorthy opened in 1991 and was built by ASCON, (Consulting engineers John B. Barry and Partners.) Ferrycarrig bridge (1980) was also by ASCON with consultants John B. Barry and Partners.

A bridge at Wexford town was built of concrete in 1959 but, following erosion, it was replaced in 1997 by a concrete & steel structure. The girders came from Italy and the bridge was built by ASCON. Consultants were John B. Barry & Partners. This 383m. bridge is the longest on the River Slaney. In addition, it is the only Slaney bridge to have received a construction award for excellence.

34

THE COUNTY SURVEYORS

Henry Brett, (County Wicklow)
Charles G. Forth, (County Carlow)
James Farrell, (County Wexford)

HENRY BRETT, (County Wicklow)

Henry Brett (c.1805-1882), civil engineer, was born at Carrowreagh, near Tobercurry, in County Sligo. Nothing is known of his early education but he is said to have 'acquired a thorough knowledge of his profession', probably receiving instruction in land surveying and estimating.

His first recorded employment was with the Waste Land Reclamation Company undertaking land improvement (drainage) in a district bordering on counties Mayo and Sligo. He then became a civil assistant working on the Boundary (later the Ordnance) Survey of Ireland.

Following the passing of the Grand Jury Act in 1834, authorising the appointment of County Surveyors, he was appointed County Surveyor for King's County (now County Offaly) and in April 1836, he transferred to County Mayo. Under Sir Richard Griffith, he executed the aplotment and valuation of County Mayo. (Griffith's Valuation defined and recorded the relative quality and value of land in each townland in Ireland.) In 1843/44, under Sir John MacNeill (q.v.), Brett carried out surveys for railway routes in the west of Ireland and projected and prepared the first plans for an (unsuccessful) Irish West Coast Railway.

During the Famine of 1846/47, as an Inspector for the Board of Public Works (Ireland), working with an establishment of some 200 engineers and upwards of 20,000 labourers, he supervised relief works in County Mayo. He held the strong conviction that the relief works were both extravagant and wasteful and had a demoralising effect on those in receipt of relief.

In October 1849, Brett was appointed County Surveyor for County Waterford and, in July 1853, he transferred to County Wicklow. Besides his County work, he was engaged on his own account on various railway projects: with George Willoughby Hemans (q.v.) on the Athenry & Tuam line, and with John Hill (q.v.) on the Midland Counties & Shannon Junction line. In 1863/64, he was Engineer for the Dublin & Baltinglass railway, a scheme that was abandoned resulting in him sustaining substantial financial loss.

He carried out many improvements in County Wicklow, notably bridges at Wicklow, Avoca and Enniskerry. The first

Seskin Bridge

Rathdrum viaduct, County Wicklow. c.1860.
This early photograph shows the method of arch construction. Timber supports have been erected and all arches are built simultaneously. This technique, first used in France in the 1700s, enables the use of thin support piers.

masonry bridge on the River Slaney, at Seskin, Glen of Imaal (1856), bears his name.

In 1869 he worked on the water supply (and later, sewerage) scheme of Bray, for which township he acted as Surveyor. Henry Brett was a founder member in August 1835 of the Civil Engineers' Society of Ireland (later the ICEI). Following the reorganisation of the ICEI in 1844, Brett served for a time on its first Council.

About 1828, Henry Brett married Catherine Cuffe of Killala, Achonry, County Sligo. Their son, Henry Charles, was an engineering graduate of the University of Dublin (1870) and another son, John H. Brett, became County Surveyor of Kildare. There is evidence that Henry Brett married a second time as, at the time of his death, his widow is noted as Mary.

Henry Brett died on 13th May, 1882, at his residence 'Rosemount', Booterstown, County Dublin, of chronic enlargement of the prostate and cystitis. He is buried in Deansgrange Cemetery, near Dublin.

CHARLES G. FORTH, (County Carlow)
Charles G. Forth was one of Charles Vignoles' earliest assistants, working with him on the Cheltenham Waterworks Survey in 1825. Forth subsequently worked with Vignoles on a variety of railway schemes in England, including the Liverpool & Chorlton Railway (1829/30). On the Dublin & Kingstown Railway survey in 1832, (for Ireland's first railway), Forth was Vignoles' senior assistant and, with Woodhouse, was left in charge of most of the detailed planning and construction work.

Charles G. Forth was appointed County Surveyor of Carlow on 17th May, 1834. He accomplished a feat of engineering skill in his construction of Tullow Bridge, which has very flat arches designed to reduce road gradient.

Tullow Bridge

It is likely that he was also involved in the construction of a similar bridge at Moatabower, upriver from Tullow on the Carlow to Hacketstown road, as this structure displays the same engineering features of flattened arches and granite finish as Tullow Bridge. A third bridge of this type crosses the River Derreen on the Hacketstown to Rathvilly road and is, presumably, his work also.

The year 1844 saw the revival of the 1825/26 scheme for a Limerick to Waterford railway, with Vignoles acting as consulting engineer for the new company. On 31st July 1844, Forth moved from Carlow to become County Surveyor for Waterford and was immediately appointed by Vignoles to head up a team which took on responsibility for completing the route surveys and preparing the detailed plans.

Charles G. Forth died suddenly in July 1845, just as the Bill to authorize construction of the line was completing its passage through Parliament.

JAMES FARRELL, (County Wexford)
James Barry Farrell (1810-1893), civil engineer, was born at Bristol on 3rd December, 1810. After serving a pupilage to the civil engineer Joseph Burke, he was engaged from 1833 to 1838 by the Board of Public Works (Ireland) as Resident Engineer on the survey and construction of the mountain road between Killarney and Kenmare, County Kerry.

On 7th March 1839, he was appointed County Surveyor of Tyrone but, shortly afterwards, on 12th August 1840, he was appointed County Surveyor of County Wexford, in which post he was to spend upwards of 50 years.

During this time, all the works in the County financed under the Grand Juries Acts were carried out to his design and specifications. These included Carrigmannon Bridge near Glynn, a masonry bridge having three 50ft. spans at a height of 120ft. above a deep ravine. He also designed a similar bridge at Cooladine, near Enniscorthy and a timber trestle bridge at Killurin, which was erected in 1842-44.

In 1846, an Act was obtained for the construction of five embankments for reclamation works at Wexford Harbour and Farrell was appointed Engineer to the Harbour Improvement Company and immediately began work in this connection under Sir John Coode (q.v.). The work included the deepening and cutting of new channels to the quays at Wexford and the construction of the two-mile long northern embankment.

Farrell also reported on improvements to the harbours at Belfast, Cork, Limerick and on reclamation work on the Castlemaine Estuary in County Kerry. Around 1862, he was appointed Engineer to the Admiralty Commissioners for Wexford Harbour.

In January 1851, Farrell completed a design for Wexford bridge over the River Slaney to replace the earlier toll bridge. This bridge (not built) was to have had a superstructure of iron girders spanning between timber trestle piers and a central drawbridge.

In 1866, the old toll bridge was replaced with a bridge built to Farrell's specifications.

During the winter of 1866/67, the wooden bridge at New Ross was swept away by ice and a new bridge, chiefly of iron, was designed by Farrell jointly with S. U. Roberts (q.v.) and Peter Burtchaell, sometime County Surveyor of Kilkenny. Again, there is no evidence that this bridge was built and it was not until 1910(?) that Lemuel Cox's wooden bridge was replaced by a concrete structure using the Hennibique reinforcing system.

Farrell was admitted to membership of the Civil Engineers' Society of Ireland on 8th September 1836 and was thus one of the earliest members of the Society (founded August 1835) that in 1844 became the Institution of Civil Engineers of Ireland. He was elected MICE on 24th May 1870.

James Barry Farrell retired in 1891 on a pension of £400 per annum. He died on 3rd January 1893 at Glena Terrace, Wexford, having been paralysed for the previous two years and was buried in Wexford.

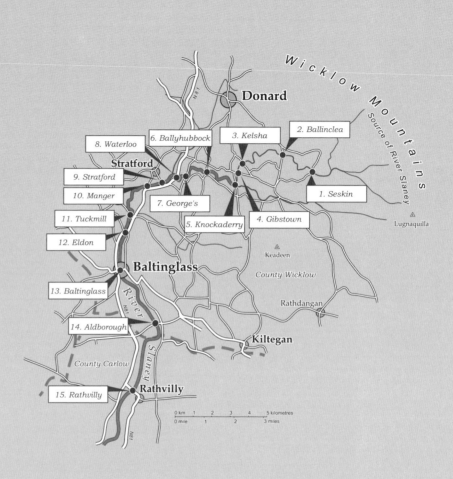

Wicklow Mountains

Source of River Slaney

Donard

8. Waterloo

6. Ballyhubbock

3. Kelsha

2. Ballinclea

Stratford

9. Stratford

1. Seskin

10. Manger

7. George's

11. Tuckmill

5. Knockaderry

4. Gibstown

Lugnaquilla

12. Eldon

Keadeen

County Wicklow

Baltinglass

13. Baltinglass

Rathdangan

River

14. Aldborough

Kiltegan

County Carlow

Slaney

15. Rathvilly

Rathvilly

0 km   1   2   3   4   5 kilometres
0 mile   1   2   3 miles

Chapter 3

Slaney Bridges of County Wicklow

SESKIN (bridge no.1)

Seisceann, a quagmire, or marshy, boggy place.

Upriver from Seskin bridge is Camara Hill, birthplace of the 1798 rebel leader, Michael Dwyer. A statue to Dwyer and his followers was unveiled at Seskin on 14th December, 2003, by An Taoiseach, Mr. Bertie Ahern, on the anniversary of Dwyer's surrender on 14th December,1803, to Mr. William Hume, M.P., at the Three Bridges, on the road between Talbotstown and Rathdangan.

The ruins of Leitrim military barracks are near Seskin bridge. This was one of five barracks constructed through County Wicklow after the rebellion of 1798. It was designed to house 200 troops but was never used as more peaceful times returned.

Seskin is the first road bridge on the River Slaney, situated at the edge of the Irish Defence Forces' artillery range in the Glen of Imaal. It bears a foundation stone that reads, *'Henry Brett, Esq., County Surveyor. Patrick Byrne, Contractor. Seskin Bridge 1856'*. Henry Brett was appointed Wicklow County Surveyor in July 1853.

This well-built masonry bridge, constructed of granite, is of three segmental arch spans. A feature is the projecting string course above the arches. Spandrel walls between the arches are of roughly-dressed field stones laid in horizontal courses. Above these, field stones are used in the parapet walls and these are capped with half-round section granite coping stones.

BALLINCLEA (bridge no.2)

Baile an tsléibhe, the town of the mountain.

Along the road between Ballinclea and Donard, a sign indicates the home place of Mary Doyle of Knockandarragh who, on 16th October 1798, became the wife of rebel leader, Michael Dwyer. After his surrender in 1803, Dwyer spent two years in Kilmainham Jail, Dublin, before being shipped to Australia. He was accompanied by his wife and two of their four children, as well as a few of his rebel comrades. He died in 1825 and his wife, Mary, died in 1861. They are buried in Waverley Cemetery, Sidney.

Also near Ballinclea bridge is Brittas Hill where Dwyer used a cave as a hideaway in '98. According to Charles Dixon in his Life of Michael Dwyer (1944), the cave had a sweeping view of the Glen and could accommodate three persons.

Ballinclea Bridge carries a road from Knockanarrigan to Donard. Similar in many ways to Seskin Bridge, although of lesser quality, the bridge at Ballinclea is most probably earlier, dating from around the 1820s. In this case, the arch ring profiles are more elliptical and there are pointed cutwaters on the upstream face. The arches have been completed by the final placing of large keystones. Once the arch rings had been completed, the temporary timber centering used to support the masonry would have been removed, thus transferring loads to the arch rings.Here, the spandrel walls have been continued up to parapet height and capped with schist stones placed upright. The approach embankments, contained between rubble walls, resist the horizontal thrust of the arches.

KELSHA (bridge no.3)

Coillseach, underwood or brushwood.

In the 1700s, Acts of Parliament stipulated a minimum road width of 12ft., (later 14ft.), and this partly accounts for the scarcity of very old bridges today. Kelsha bridge, on a minor route, seems to have escaped these laws and is a rare Slaney bridge of its kind.

Kelsha Bridge is narrow and hump-backed, and dates from around 1780. The bridge carries a minor road between Knockanarrigan and Donard, bypassing Davidstown. The three arch profiles are nearly circular, thus the rise to span ratio is greater. The greater the span the greater the rise, which results in the central arch rising more than the flanking arches, thus forming a humpbacked structure. The voussoirs (arch stones) are of worked granite.

On the downstream face, there are square section cutwaters roughly tapering to parapet level, whilst on the upstream face, the cutwaters are pointed. The parapets are formed of rough stones set vertically.

Unsympathetic concrete repairs have been carried out and concrete skirts placed around piers but, nevertheless, the bridge in its setting has significant scenic value.

GIBSTOWN (bridge no.4)
This place is noted as Ballygibb in 1619.

St. Palladius arrived in Arklow in 431. He established a Christian church near Donard at Church Mountain and, in the following year, St. Patrick constructed one at Donoughmore.

In the 1830s, the traveller Samuel Lewis wrote that the parish of Donoughmore had 4,130 inhabitants and that the area had excellent tillage and pasture lands. Great numbers of calves were fattened here and large quantities of butter produced for the Dublin market.

Parapet walls of a masonry bridge sometimes bear a foundation stone or commemorative plaque, but the effects of weathering over time make it difficult to interpret the wording. Here we have a plaque which at least informs us the bridge was erected in 1822 and that there was an engineer and overseer involved. Included in the wording is P Valin... Eng., which could possibly be 'P Valintine, Engineer'. Sometimes the promoter of the bridge (maybe the local squire) is mentioned or the Grand Jury or local authority who provided the finance.

This typical three-span masonry arch bridge bears some resemblance to Ballinclea Bridge, both having being erected around the same time. However, Gibstown has half-round cutwaters on the upstream side only and has a slightly different treatment of the parapets.

The arch rings are formed of ashlar (worked stone) masonry with a large keystone at the top. Some of the ashlar was used to start the spandrel walls, but coursed rubble was then used for the upper sections of the walls.

KNOCKADERRY (bridge no.5)

Cnoc an Doire, hill of the oak wood; 'Knockederrie', in 1587.

The Glen of Imaal, from earliest times, had vast tracts of woodland as testified in such placenames as *Derrynamuck* and *Knockaderry*.

The Normans introduced the concept of private ownership of land and its produce, i.e. trees. Deer hunting through woods was a royal sport in England and the forests of Dublin and Wicklow came under 'forest laws' and many deer parks were established. Forests were also used as cover by Irish rebels and were recognized as a threat by the authorities. In 1399, Richard II had 5,000 men cut a track through the Leinster forest from the River Barrow to the Wicklow coast, (presumably to Arklow).

This crossing is a 50ft span pre-stressed concrete road bridge of composite construction, the deck being carried on inverted T-beams spanning between the abutments. The bridge was erected in the 1970s by Wicklow County Council, the county engineer at the time being Joe Forristal. The bridge replaced an earlier masonry bridge damaged by floods.

BALLYHUBBOCK (bridge no.6)

Baile Hobag. Hob, a form of 'Robert', Robert being the name of a likely 13th century settler.

On Jacob Nevill's County Wicklow map of 1760, Ballyhubbock is shown as the first bridge on the River Slaney and it was one of only two bridges (with Manger) above Baltinglass at that time.

Near the bridge is the remains of a motte & bailey (a Norman fortified residence) and, at Castleruddery, the O'Tooles once had a castle guarding the entrance to Imaal.

Charles Dixon's book, *Life of Michael Dwyer* (1944), says that the 1798 rebel leader received schooling at Ballyhubbock. A schoolmate was John Jackson and the two remained close friends despite Jackson later becoming a Yeoman. Dwyer prevented the burning of Jackson's home, Spinans House, in '98 and saved his friend's life at the battle of Hacketstown in June of that year.

Nevill's 1760 map indicates a bridge here and some of the bridge's features confirm its age. Typically, the pointed cutwaters are taken up to parapet level to provide added resistance to floodwaters. In early narrow bridges, pedestrian refuges would have been provided at the tops of the cutwaters.

The three segmental arches are formed of cut granite (most likely quarried locally) and the spandrel walls are built from random rubble or fieldstone.

There is an additional smaller arch, carrying the roadway over a small stream that enters the Slaney near the bridge site, which possibly pre-dates the main structure. Concrete skirts have been placed around the piers and abutments in more recent times to protect them against scour from floodwaters.

GEORGE'S (bridge no.7)

Erected around 1820, this bridge may have been named in honour of the visit to Ireland in 1821 of King George IV (1762-1830). The King returned to England from the newly-constructed Royal Harbour at Dún Laoghaire and the town was renamed 'Kingstown' in his honour. (The name reverted to Dún Laoghaire in 1921).

The bridge has a fine single segmental arch of 40ft. span with a large keystone. The heavy abutments and retaining walls resist the considerable horizontal thrust from the arch. Whereas the arch ring is formed with high quality cut granite, the spandrel walls are of rubble construction. The parapet walls, which are splayed outwards at the ends of the bridge, are topped with granite slabs. Tunnels in the approach embankments pro-vide access for livestock and also act as flood relief conduits. Substantial wall supports (buttresses) have been added to counteract the tendency of the fill material in the abut-ments to bulge outwards.

King George IV

WATERLOO (bridge no.8)

Arthur Wellesley, Duke of Wellington

This bridge (which is sometimes called *Wellington Bridge*) is thought to be named in celebration of the defeat of Napoleon's army by the Duke of Wellington at the Battle of Waterloo in Belgium on 18th June, 1815. Over 48,500 men were either killed or wounded that day. Afterwards, the area of the battlefield was given to the Wellington family by the newly formed State of the United Kingdom of the Netherlands.

This single 48ft span masonry arch bridge is the largest single-span masonry bridge on the Slaney. The arch rings in the main span are formed from good quality cut granite and the spandrel walls are of coursed rubble extending upwards to parapets topped with a random arrangement of rubble stone.

STRATFORD (bridge no.9)

Áth na sráide, ford of the street.

On Jacob Nevill's 1760 map of County Wicklow, there is no river crossing or road to Stratford-on-Slaney as the village was not built at that time.

Today, Stratford Bridge provides access to the village of Stratford-on-Slaney from the Baltinglass-Dublin road. Though sometimes referred to as 'Building Bridge', it is listed by the local authority as Stratford Bridge.

Robert Stratford came to Ireland in 1660 from Stratford-on-Avon. He settled at Baltinglass and acquired estates in Leinster and Munster before his death in 1669.
His son, Edward, added Belan in County Kildare to the family estates.
William of Orange, on his march to Limerick, stayed at Belan and Edward Stratford donated 2,000 sheep and 200 cattle towards the support of the King's army.

Edward's son, John Stratford, was created Baron of Baltinglass in 1763 and Earl of Aldborough in 1777. He was M.P. for Baltinglass and Sheriff of counties Wicklow, Kildare, Carlow and Wexford. His estates, in seven counties, consisted of 28,000 acres.

His son, Edward Stratford, built the village of Stratford-on-Slaney c.1783, its name linking the village with the family's ancestral home, Stratford-on-Avon, in England. He established linen and cotton mills on the banks of the Slaney and Stratford-on-Slaney was laid out in streets and squares with a public lighting system. It also had three churches (Protestant, Catholic and Presbyterian), representing the diversity of the large workforce employed in the mills, many of whom came from Scotland and England.

In 1837, over 1,000 people were employed but by 1850 the industry had collapsed, with the arrival of more modern working methods. The ruins of the mill can be seen today on the banks of the Slaney.

The Earl of Stratford title died with the death of the sixth Earl in 1876. He had resided at Stratford Lodge, now the site of Baltinglass Golf Club, and the Aldborough family mausoleum is still to be seen today at Baltinglass Abbey.

The first outbreak of the 1798 rebellion in County Wicklow took place at Stratford-on-Slaney on the 24th May that year. The rebels were dispersed with about 100 killed and the failure to capture the mills and use them as a fortress was a severe setback for the rebels.

An earlier bridge on the site was washed away in 1966 and eventually replaced in concrete in 1989-90 by Wicklow County Council. Like Knockaderry upstream, this bridge is of composite construction, a reinforced concrete deck being carried on pre-stressed concrete inverted T-beams spanning 65ft between abutments.

MANGER (bridge no.10)

Name possibly derived from *'mainséar'* (a manger), or
'mainnear' (a cattle enclosure).

On Moll's Map of 1714, this river crossing is marked as 'Manger ford'. The present bridge (dating from c.1750) retains most of its original structure and, as such, it is possibly the oldest bridge on the River Slaney.

On Jacob Nevill's 1760 map of County Wicklow, Manger and Ballyhubbock are the only two bridges on the Slaney above Baltinglass.

The link road connecting Manger to the main road was built as a famine relief scheme, organised by Rev. John Marchbanks, a charitable pastor, who himself fell victim to famine fever and died at Stratford-on-Slaney, aged 30 years, in 1847.

Built in granite, Manger Bridge has five arches of varying profile, with pointed cutwaters on the upstream face only, the two middle ones being extended upwards to the top of the parapet walls, which are capped with granite coping stones.

There is a strong indication that the bridge has been widened during its lifetime and extra arches introduced to accommodate floodwaters. This would have been likely undertaken in the 1820s.

TUCKMILL (bridge no.11)

Called Tokmyll in 1541.

The name shows there was a 'tucking' mill for cloth nearby, built by the Cistercians, who came to Baltinglass in 1148. They cleared huge areas of forest and Baltinglass Abbey included 59,000 acres of farmland at that time. On Jacob Nevill's 1760 map of County Wicklow, this place is shown as a ford crossing.

The present four-arch masonry bridge carries a minor road across the Slaney and was built around 1780. It is constructed in coursed rubble with dressed granite in the roughly semi-circular arches. There are tall pointed cutwaters on the upstream face. The parapets have semi-dressed granite coping stones. This is a relatively rare late 18th-century lightly trafficked road bridge that melts successfully into the surrounding rural landscape - another way of saying that it is very overgrown and neglected! There is some suggestion that the bridge has been widened, and this would probably have been done to provide better access for agricultural transport and machinery from the main road to the surrounding farmland.

ELDON (bridge no.12)

This bridge has a foundation stone bearing the words, 'Eldon Bridge'. As the bridge was erected around the same time as nearby bridges on the Slaney with names such as *Waterloo* and *George's*, it is possible that this name refers to John Scott, 1st Earl of Eldon, who was Lord Chancellor of England, for almost 27 years, between 1801 and 1827. He was born at Newcastle in 1751 and died in 1838. He was regarded as the most learned lawyer of his day.

On Jacob Nevill's 1760 Wicklow map, the road to Dublin from Baltinglass was on the left bank of the river, through Sruhaun townland. A Turnpike (toll) road connecting Carlow, Baltinglass, Blessington and Dublin was built following an Act passed by King George IV in 1829.

John Scott, 1st Earl of Eldon

This three-arch masonry bridge carries the N81 national route over the Slaney about one mile to the north of Baltinglass. The present bridge was erected around 1829 and is well constructed of coursed rubble with dressed granite voussoirs (arch stones), the largest arch having a span of 26ft. There is also one flood relief arch. The parapet is also in coursed rubble with semi-dressed granite coping stones. There are rounded cutwaters on the upstream face of the bridge. Guard rails have been installed to prevent 'parapet-bashing' by vehicles.

BALTINGLASS (bridge no.13)

Bealach Conglais, the pass or road of Cúglas, master of hounds for the King of Ireland.

Baltinglass Hill has a cairn under which are 5 burial chambers dating back to 2000 B.C. The cairn was excavated in the 1930s by the National Museum and was found to measure 84ft. (north/south) and 91ft. (east/west).

The Cistercian Order established an abbey at Baltinglass in 1148, having been granted a site by Diarmaid MacMurchadha. The Abbey farm included 59,000 acres and the monks carried on an agricultural business in conjunction with a religious life, exporting large quantities of wool to Italy from the port of Arklow. The monks changed the course of the River Slaney at Baltinglass and built a weir to operate a corn mill. The Abbey survived until the confiscation of monastery lands by Henry VIII in the 1530s and the lands were granted in 1541 to Thomas Eustace, Lord Kilcullen, who owned half of County Kildare.

The old Cistercian millworks at Baltinglass later became the site of Morrin's milling business. Morrin's mill operated for many years as the largest milling operation in west Wicklow. It was demolished in recent times and a block of apartments was built on the site.

Baltinglass was much involved in the rebellion of 1798 and, today, a plaque marks the site of the jail in '98, which stood beside Baltinglass bridge. At a shootout at a cottage in Derrynamuck in the Glen of Imaal, in February 1799, rebel leader Michael Dwyer, alone, escaped. Seven of his captured comrades were executed at Baltinglass.

In 1899, Mr. Edward P. O'Kelly, J.P., a nationalist merchant from Baltinglass, was elected the first chairman of Wicklow county council. In 1902, Mr. Kelly laid the foundation stone for the Sam McAllister monument in Baltinglass, in memory of the events at Derrynamuck, where McAllister sacraficed himself so that Dwyer could escape. A huge

crowd attended the occasion and special trains from Dublin were laid on for the event.

In the 1830s, the traveller, Samuel Lewis, wrote that Baltinglass had 256 houses with 1,670 residents. Baltinglass had *'four principal streets, was amply supplied with water from springs and, on the road from Dublin, by Tullow to Wexford, enjoyed a considerable traffic. The town is pleasantly situated in a romantic vale watered by the Slaney, over which is a stone bridge of three arches connecting those parts of it which are on opposite banks of the river.'* At this time, Baltinglass had two M.P.s in Parliament, a courthouse, bridewell and infantry barracks.

During the Famine, the following was written in February 1847 concerning work relief schemes at Baltinglass, by The Engineer's Office, Arklow: *'There are 500 men employed on Relief Works. They are, generally speaking, a most inflammable community, chiefly consisting of the rejected from other districts and counties, bound by no ties of connexion or character, living on a property where there is neither a resident landlord or agent. In summer, they earn some money by cutting turf, and also during the hurry of the harvest. During the remainder of the year, they idle, steal or beg'.*

Baltinglass Bridge is a freestanding three-arch shallow humpback bridge, built in the 1770s. The segmental arch rings span between piers with pointed cutwaters. The voussoirs in the arch rings are dressed granite of alternating sizes. There is some architectural detailing consisting of a small roundel or oriel feature in the spandrel walls over the piers. This would suggest that an architect was consulted, but experienced journeymen masons were well capable of such embellishments. The bridge appears to be in original condition, apart from the concreting of the arch soffits, or underside, of the structure.

ALDBOROUGH (Holdenstown)   (bridge no.14)

This place is called *'Holdingstown'* on Jacob Nevill's 1760 map of County Wicklow and a ford crossing is shown here at that time.

Ordnance field books of 1839 state: *'In Mountneil townland are the remains of a large mansion... burnt by accident about 40 years ago'.*

Reverend Paul Stratford lived at Mount Neil, one of the oldest of Aldborough residences. A man of great faith, he prevented local people from trying to save his furniture when the big house went on fire, saying *'Never fly in the face of Heaven, my friends. When the Almighty resolved to burn my house, He most certainly intended to destroy my furniture. I am resigned – the Lord's will be done'.* Afterwards, his strength of faith must have been tested on discovering that the insurance company refused to pay any portion of damages caused by the fire, presumably because of his lack of interest in saving his property.

In 1886, the GSWR built a railway line from Sallins to Tullow which crossed the Slaney near the border between counties Wicklow and Carlow. The branch was closed in 1959 and the iron bridge removed.

Aldborough Bridge has a foundation stone on the upstream wall bearing the words 'Aldborough Bridge 182...' This bridge is one of only four old Slaney bridges with a written foundation stone. Curiously, all four are in County Wicklow. The others are Seskin, Gibstown and Eldon.

This bridge is on a connecting road between the N81 and the R747. The arch rings of this three-span masonry bridge contain finely dressed granite voussoirs (arch stones) with a prominent keystone and indicate that quality masons were employed. The bridge could have been widened on the downstream side as the spandrel walls appear to be constructed differently. That on the downstream side has dressed stone laid in courses, whereas that on the upstream side is comprised of a much rougher stone or so-called 'fieldstone'. The parapet walls are capped with upright fieldstones interspersed with larger squared stones. There are pointed cutwaters on the upstream face as is normal for such multi-span masonry bridges.

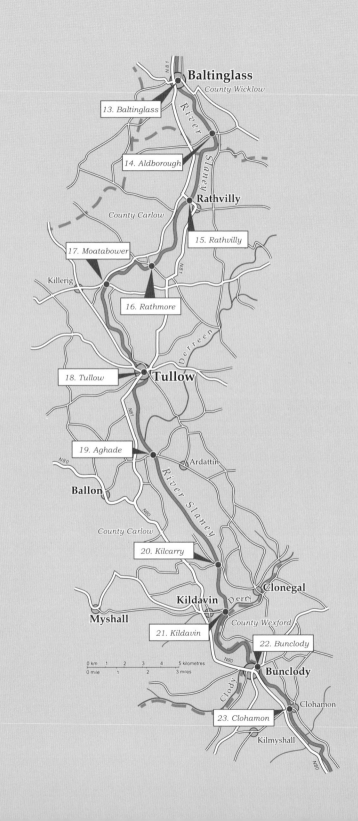

Chapter 4

Slaney Bridges of County Carlow

RATHVILLY (bridge no.15)

Ráth Bhile, fort of the old tree.

The *ráth* is thought to have been part of a series of earthen forts that included Eagle Hill, Clonmore, Tullow and Castlemore. *Bile* referred to a large tree held in veneration, usually where chiefs were inaugurated, or games celebrated. Trees were very important in ancient times and the Brehon Laws categorised them as scrub trees, common trees and chieftain trees. ('Chieftain' trees were: Oak, Hazel, Holly, Yew, Ash, Pine and Apple). To cut a branch meant a fine of a yearling heifer and to cut down a tree meant a fine of a milk cow.

At a well north of Rathvilly Motte, St. Patrick baptised Crimthann, King of Leinster and his family, in 450.

The dominant feature of the area is Lisnavagh Estate, where generations of local people were employed over many years. Benjamin Bunbury, a native of Cheshire, settled at Killerig in the 1600s. His son, William, lived at Lisnavagh.

The local D'Israeli school (presently the parish centre) is named after Benjamin D'Israeli (1766-1814) who purchased Beechy Park House and left £1,000 to build a school. He also left a £2,000 trust fund to pay teachers. His nephew Benjamin was twice Prime Minister of England and three times Chancellor of the Exchequer.

In recent times, Rathvilly is known for its success in the national Tidy Towns Competition, having won the National Title in 1961, 1963 and 1968.

The green in Rathvilly has a monument to Kevin Barry, a medical student from the area, who was executed in Dublin in 1920 during the War of Independence.

The N81 crosses the Slaney just to the north-east of the village of Rathvilly. Towards the centre of the bridge, the spans /rises of the six elliptical arches increase to 18ft / 5ft 10in giving a gentle humped appearance. As with many masonry bridges on main routes, that at Rathvilly has been repaired (in concrete) to halt deterioration of the stonework.

Although erected as long ago as 1800, the bridge has faired reasonably well, due largely to the quality of the original construction. The six arch rings are well formed with cut stone voussoirs (arch stones) and have triple keystones at their crowns. The pointed cutwaters are carried upwards in the form of pyramidal-shaped stonework.

The spandrel walls are formed of cut stone laid in courses, but the faces have received a concrete coating to seal them against the weather and to prevent vegetation growth in the original mortar joints. This treatment, although considered necessary, does nothing for the aesthetic value of the structure. The underside of the arches have also been sprayed with concrete, a technique known as 'guniting'. The parapet walls have also been repaired with concrete. The older lighting brackets on the parapets have been supplemented with modern lighting that is out of keeping with the age of the bridge.

RATHMORE (bridge no.16)

Ráth Mór, great fort; residence of King Colman in the 6th century.

Ordnance field books of 1839 state :
'It (Rathmore) *is the property of Thomas Bunbury, Esq. of Moyle. The river Slaney bounds it on the south side. There is one Gentleman's seat, called Rathmore House, the residence of Charles Putland, Esq., J.P.'* Benjamin Bunbury, of Chester, established the first family seat at Killerig House in the late 1600s. His son William lived at Lisnavagh, Rathvilly. In 1846, Thomas Bunbury died leaving a 6,000-acre estate in Kellistown, Rathmore and Rathvilly.

On Rathmore bridge, the Ordnance field books of 1839 state: *'Over the Slaney at the junction of Rathmore parish with Tuckamine and Ballybit Big townslands in Rathvilly parish. A good substantial bridge of 4 arches. The water runs under all 4 arches'.*

There is a salmon pool above the bridge known today as Skelton's Hole. Lewis, in the 1830s, wrote of it: *'Situated about 5 chains above Rathmore Bridge in the river Slaney, and is so named from the circumstance of one Skelton having been drowned in it about 100 years ago'.*

On Lewis' 1830s map, another bridge across the Slaney in this area is indicated at the Bullring. A road from the Bullring crossed the Slaney and came out at Kilmagarvoge Cross on the Carlow to Hacketstown road. This bridge (and road) are not on Philips' map of 1885.

A reinforced concrete bridge whose design is typical of road bridges erected between the wars in many parts of Ireland. The stark nature of the beams and abutments is offset by the rather more attractive pierced balustraded parapets.

There are two masonry arches (of the original bridge) on the flood plain, probably dating from the early 1800s. There were originally four masonry arches spanning the river and these could have been damaged during the Civil War (1921-22), necessitating their replacement in the late 1920s by the present structure.

MOATABOWER (bridge no.17)

Móta Bodhar, the deaf(ening) moat - possibly refers to the sound of the river in spate.

The Ordnance field books of 1839 state: *'Moatabower ford – On the road from Rathvilly to Carlow at Straboe Cross. It leads over the Slaney into Downings townland, in Tullowphelim parish. This is a dangerous ford in time of flood and several people have been drowned here'.*

Moatabower bridge, on the Carlow to Hacketstown road, is one of only two bridges on the River Slaney (with Tullow) faced entirely with cut granite. Such bridges were expensive to build. Like Tullow, its flattened arches display great engineering skill and were designed with minimum gradient to facilitate traffic.

The walls of Moatabower bridge presently show movement of stones, brought on by heavy traffic use.

As with Tullow Bridge, the arches of the bridge at Moatabower are of very low rise to span ratio, i.e. a 'flat' arch. This indicates a high level of understanding by the designer of the way in which arches withstand the loads imposed upon them and is a considerable act of faith in the ability of the single pier and abutments to withstand the horizontal thrusts.

Both arches and spandrel walls are constructed of large semi-ashlar blocks of granite and there is a string course placed immediately above the crowns of the arches. The spandrel walls are continued upwards to form the parapets.

There are semi-circular cutwaters on both faces of the central pier.

The inscription 'T.C.1841' on the parapet suggests the date of construction but leaves us guessing as to who the designer was. The County Surveyor at the time was Charles G. Forth and it is likely that he was involved as he was the designer of the bridge downstream at Tullow.

TULLOW (bridge no.18)

Tulach, little hill. *Tullowphelim*, from a tribe descended from Feilimí, brother of Crimthan, first Christian King of Leinster.

In 1314, the Augustinian Order was granted a house and three acres of land in the village of St. John (Templeowen) near Tullow. Their abbey grew to 44 acres with another 60 acres in Mallardiston. Monastery lands were confiscated in 1536 by Henry VIII and the Augustinian lands at Tullow were granted to the Earl of Ormond. The Augustinians, without a monastery, continued in Tullow until 1799. Tullow Castle, built c.1180 by Hugh De Lacy, was at the site of the Protestant church. It was attacked and taken by Cromwellian forces in 1650. Stone from it (and the abbey) was used to construct a barracks in Barrack Street, the site of which later became occupied by the courthouse. Dr. Daniel Delany (1747-1814), Bishop of the Diocese of Kildare & Leighlin, founded the

Order of Patrician Brothers at Tullow. He was resident in the town during the rebellion of 1798 when Wexford rebels, Fr. John Murphy and James Gallagher, were captured in the area and executed in Tullow on 2nd July that year.

Mount Wolseley, (then on the opposite side of the road to the present-day establishment), was burned by rebels in 1798. The present Mount Wolseley, built by Sir Thomas Wolseley in 1864, was purchased by the Patrician Brothers in 1925. Today the property is a championship golf course owned by the Morrissey family.

During the reign of James 1, 'a licence to keep taverns and sell wine and ardent spirits was granted to James Knowles of Carlow, merchant, and Rose his wife, during their

lives, within the town of Tullaghphelim, and two miles round'.

In the 1830s, there were 1,929 people living in Tullow which *'comprises two main streets and a few lanes, in which are 305 houses, mostly of inferior description'*. At this time, Tullow was a main constabulary police station. The town had two breweries belonging to Mr. Carter and Mr. Roche and the flourmill of Messrs. Doyle & Pim ground 10,000 barrels of wheat annually.

The old Presbyterian church at the bridge now houses Tullow museum.

TULLOW BRIDGE

Tullow is an ancient river crossing, being on the Slighe Chualann, the roadway south

through west Wicklow from Bohernabreena to the Slaney and Barrow valleys.

A visitor in 1680 wrote that the tenant of the castle, William Crutchley, J.P., 'repaired the town bridge which is of stone with arches'.

Ordnance field books of 1839 refer to a stone bridge with five arches bearing the inscription: 'This bridge was built by Mr. Thomas Nowlan of Rathvaran, farmer, in the year 1767; Sir Richard Butler, Bart; Thomas Bunbury, Robert Eustace, Esq; Messrs. Robert Lecky and John Brewster, overseers'. In 1770, the Grand Jury of County Carlow thanked Mr. John Semple for drawing and planning the bridge, overseeing the work 'which is completely finished in a very strong and handsome manner, and at much less Expence than they apprehend it would have been done for, without his Directions and Advice'.

In 1842, the county surveyor, Mr. Charles G. Forth, read a paper to the Institution of Civil Engineers outlining gradient problems with Tullow bridge. Forth altered the bridge which, when finished, was tested with carts bearing loads of 35cwt. The work cost £485.

The present bridge has four spans with extra relief channels and the structure appears to have replaced the old bridge of the 1840s.

The bridge was strengthened in the 1980s by Carlow County Council and a flood relief plan is presently proposed for the town.

Tullow and Moatabower are the only two bridges on the Slaney with flattened arches and faced entirely with cut granite.

In 1842, Charles G. Forth, was faced at Tullow with the task of replacing an early masonry bridge that had steep approaches and a narrow carriageway of 18ft. As to raise the level of the approaches would have hindered the passage of potential floodwaters, Forth decided to use very flat segmental arches, the rise to span ratio of the central 28ft span arch being only 0.09. The inclination of the roadway was thus reduced from 1 in 7 to 1 in 40, the recommended maximum gradient for horse-drawn coaches. The bridge was also widened to provide a clear carriageway of 28ft. The work was carried out in undressed rubble granite with an ashlar face. Tullow bridge has significant architectural merit with simple but effective detailing over the piers and pointed cutwaters.

AGHADE (bridge no.19)

Áth Fhadhat, Fadhat's ford.

In the 6th century, a battle was fought here over fishing rights on the River Slaney. One of the contestants, a chieftain named *Fadhat*, was defeated and killed.

Ordnance field books of 1839 state that Aghade townland...*'is the property of Lord Downes of Bert, near Athy. It is let in farms of from 5 to 20 acres at 25s. per acre. The fields are badly sheltered but are very productive'*.

The Protestant church at Aghade occupies the probable site of an 1151 abbey of the Nuns of the Order of St. Augustine.

Downriver from Aghade is Altamont Gardens, one of County Carlow's main tourist attractions. It is managed by the Office of Public Works, the gardens having been left to the State by Mrs. Corona North. The grounds contain a man-made lake and plants & trees from around the world.

On Aghade bridge, Ordnance field books of 1839 refer to *'..an old bridge of 5 arches, well built, about 100 ft. long and 30 ft. wide. It is about 20 ft. above the bed of the river'*.

Aghade is the oldest Slaney bridge in County Carlow, (built c.1760), and is situated at one of the most scenic spots on the river. It was renovated c.1825, when the centre arch was rebuilt.

The greater span and rise of the central arch gives the bridge a hump-backed appearance. The arch rings are comprised of good quality cut stones (voussoirs) with triple key stones at their crowns. The underside of the arches have been sprayed with concrete to prevent leaching of the mortar and fill and to discourage further movements in the masonry. The spandrel walls are of granite rubble and the parapets topped with granite blocks. There are rock outcrops at the bridge site, thus there has been no need to underpin the piers.

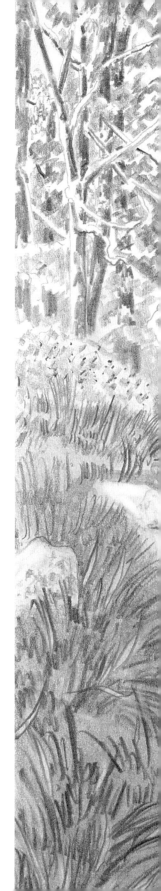

KILCARRY (bridge no.20)

Coill Carraig, Wood of the rock.

Ordnance field books 1839, on Kilcarry townland, read: *'It is the property of Jas. Denham, Co. Fermanagh. Agent, John De Renzy, Clonegall. Size of farms, 3 to 60 Ir. Acres. Rent, from 25s. to 35s. per acre'* and, on Kilcarry Bridge: *'A good stone bridge of 5 arches, faced with chiselled granite'*.

In the Down Survey of 1656, Clonegal (Kilcarry) is the only bridge shown across the Slaney (or any other river in Wexford) at that time.

Kingsmill Moore, fisherman and author of the angling classic, *'A man may fish'* (1960), lived for many years at the Mill House, Kilcarry.

At this location, the river runs between high banks and the crossing required inclined approaches at both ends of the bridge and high piers. The three main arches are well formed with cut stone granite voussoirs (tapered arch stones) and there are two additional flood arches. The spandrel walls are of coursed stone and there are pointed cutwaters with pyramidal tops on the upstream side only. There is evidence of repairs to the parapet walls, which have been topped with cement mortar. The bridge was erected around 1800.

KILDAVIN (New Bridge) (bridge no.21)

Cill Damhán, Church of St. Damhán, a saint of about the 5th century.

Ordnance field books of 1839 say of Kildavin townland: *'It is the property of Counsellor John Hatchell, Dublin, and is let at from 10s. to £2 per acre in farms varying from 10 to 100 acres. William St. George, Esq. And Mr. J. Malone are the principal lessees. It is mostly pasture land, grazing sheep and black cattle'.*

Kildavin village *'consists of a few clean-looking houses on the road from Tullow to Newtownbarry, about 2 miles from the latter town. It contains a neat church, a Roman Catholic chapel, a National School and 3 public houses'.*

Cardinal Francis Spellman (1889-1967), Archbishop of New York, was grandson of Ellen Kehoe of Sherwood, Kilbride, who emigrated to America. The Cardinal donated Kildavin Hall to the village and the local G.A.A. Park is named after him.

The area once had a forge, cornstore, woolstore and a mill at Ballypierce. The sandpits along this stretch of the river Slaney are unique in being one of only two locations in Ireland possessing 'high beach' sand, (along with Lahinch, County Clare).

The Ordnance field books of 1839 refer to the 'New Bridge – a good stone bridge of 6 arches on the road to Clonegall'. Today, this bridge is also referred to as 'Young's Bridge'. In Charles Bowden's *Tour through Ireland'* (1791), there is reference to an earlier bridge structure. Bowden was introduced to a *'most remarkable man who lived at Johnstown* (near Clonegal) *named Charles Dunroche, and although he had little education, he was much esteemed in the neighbourhood as dentist, physician, attorney and land surveyor. He was also a cabinet-maker and a stonemason.*

It was from a design of his drawing that a new bridge was erected in preference to many other designs, at the confluence of the rivers Slaney and Derry. At this bridge, he worked as a stonemason'. In his house, *'which was a small but tastefully laid out cabin, he had a surgery and a shop in which he sold medicines'.*

A fine masonry arch bridge of fairly standard design. It straddles the border between the counties of Carlow and Wexford and replaced an earlier structure, hence the name 'New Bridge'. It was constructed c.1800. The segmental arch rings are formed with cut stone granite (semi-ashlar) and, like Kilcarry, the pointed cutwaters upstream and downstream have pyramidal tops. A mass concrete slab has been used to raise the parapets. There are plaques set into the parapet walls, but there does not appear to be any inscription.

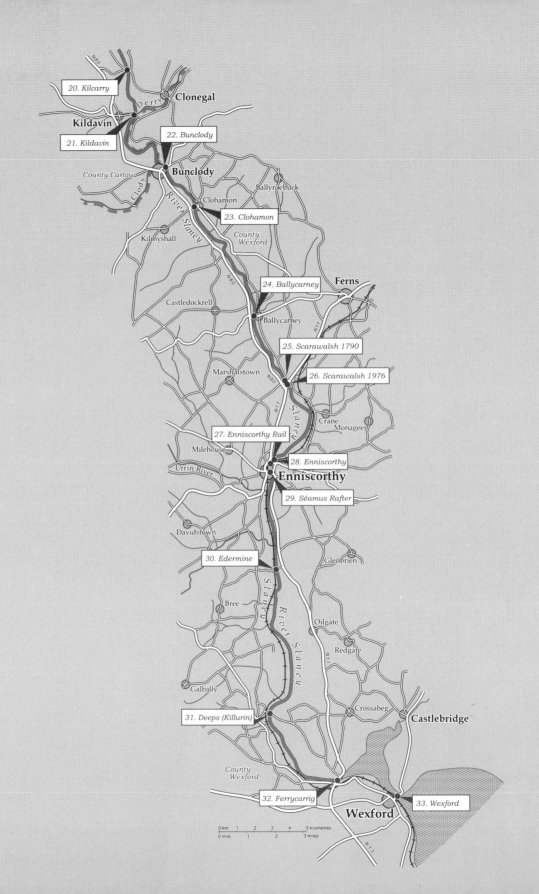

Chapter 5

Slaney Bridges of County Wexford

BUNCLODY (Slaney Bridge) (no.22)

Bun Clóidí, where the River Clody joins the River Slaney.

Since the 1720s, the town was known alternately as *Newtownbarry* and *Bunclody*. Following a Council plebiscite in 1950, the town officially became known as *Bunclody*.

The Caomhánach family moved to France following the Williamite War and their lands were occupied by Mark Owens from 1691-1718. James Barry, Sovereign of Naas, purchased the lands in 1719 and the 10,000 acres were formed into an estate. His daughter Judith married John Maxwell in 1719, and it was they who named the town *'Newtownbarry'*, in honour of Judith's father.

John Maxwell was created Baron Farnham in 1756 and the Maxwell family remained until 1854, at which time the estate suffered difficulties and was sold that year by the Encumbered Estates Court to Samuel Ashton. He, in 1861, sold the estate (which then included the town) to the Hall-Dare family. Newtownbarry House, on the site of an older house at Woodfield, was designed by W.H. Lanyon.

The Town Mall is traditionally thought to have been the brainchild of Lady Lucy Farnham (née Mountnorris) who was responsible for laying out walks through the

woods – one wood is known as Lucy's Wood and a bower is called The Mosshouse, (on O.S. map it is *The Lady's Seat*). She used to be carried through the woods in a sedan chair. This chair can be seen today in the county museum, Enniscorthy.

Sir Murchadh Caomhánach was killed at the battle of Ballinvegga near New Ross in 1643. His daughter, Eilíonóir, is the subject of love poems written by her lover, the north Wexford poet, Cearúll Óg Ó Dálaigh, and she is remembered today in the song 'Eibhlín a Rúin'. The first appearance in print of the words '*Céad Míle Fáilte*' occurs in this song.

In the 1830s, Bunclody had 250 houses with 1,430 residents and '*the whole has a cheerful and thriving appearance*'.

Slaney Bridge was constructed by the Maxwell family in the 1790s. Up to 1875, the bridge was about two thirds of its present width and the authorities proposed widening it. The bridge, at that time, was dangerous and the rule was that people had to wait at either end until vehicles passed. It was described as a '*miserable bridge which is a disgrace to the progress of the age*' and people crossed '*with constant risk of their lives*'.

The bridge was widened in 1875 and the extension work can be seen from underneath. A 1798 memorial marks the spot where human bones were unearthed during construction work. Considered to be the remains of people killed in 1798, the skeletons were re-interred in St. Mary's Catholic Cemetery.

A small portion of the bridge is in County Carlow at the point where the Clody river joins the Slaney. In years gone by, there was a footbridge crossing the Clody, a few yards downriver from Slaney Bridge.

A short distance upriver, at the *bridge meadow*, there once existed a metal bridge across the Slaney which was constructed in 1854. It was for horse-drawn carriages and connected Newtownbarry House to the Protestant church in the town. It was destroyed in the winter floods of 1965-66.
Slaney Bridge has the most impressive parapet stones of all Slaney bridges.

The river is now wider at this point and the bridge in the town has six main spans and two small arches on the flood plain.
There are pointed cutwaters on the upstream face and flat-topped square dividers on the downstream face. Some 365 hammer-dressed granite stones were used to cap the parapet walls.

CLOHAMON (no.23)

Cloch Ámainn, Hamon's castle, named after a 12th century Norman.

Local lands were granted in the 16th century to an Englishman, Thomas Masterson. His son, Sir Richard, sold the estate c.1625 to Sir George Calvert, Lord Baltimore, for £1,600. He had received grant of lands in County Longford but moved to Clohamon in preference. He was also granted lands in Newfoundland and became the only Catholic to be granted a fiefdom in North America by an English king, the province of Maryland.

Clohamon, the centre of the Calvert Estate, was one of the largest towns in north Wexford in the 1650s.

The Fair at Clohamon was held once a year and became established as an occasion for faction-fighting.

Samuel Lewis wrote in the 1830s : *'Clohamon is a neat and thriving village of recent origin, and the population is chiefly employed in the large flour and cotton mills of Mr. William Lewis'*. The mill operated until 1904 and was then derelict until it was purchased for use as a chicken rearing unit in 1960.

Underneath Clohamon bridge there is a salmon pass with a fish counter and, in recent years, a second pass was built in the weir by Slaney Rod Fishers.

Lewis also referred to *'the parish of Kilrush, watered by the river Slaney, over which are two stone bridges, one connecting it with Newtownbarry, the other crossing the river at Clohamon'*.

The arch rings have been formed using fairly roughly cut blocks of granite stone (voussoirs). Three arches display shale spacers between arch stones but the other two arches have had their stones concreted over, a practice frowned on by building conservationists. The view from under the bridge seems to show that the bridge was widened at some point in its history. The walls are of coursed rubble and the parapets are topped with schist stones placed vertically. The small flood arch in the approach embankment serves as a conduit for winter flood waters. Pointed cutwaters are on the upstream face, the central ones having been later extended up to parapet level.

BALLYCARNEY (bridge no.24)

Baile Uí Chearnaigh, Ó Cearnaigh's homestead.

Lands at Ballycarney were granted to the Mayor of Dublin, Sir James Carroll, in 1612. In 1635, Sir William Brereton commented on Sir James Carroll's house, *'A new and stately house, which hath almost sunk him by the charge of building the same'*. It was probably destroyed during the 1641 rebellion.

The Civil Survey records in 1654 say of Ballycarney, *'A large stone house, two mills and two wears upon the river Slane(y)'*.

Lewis wrote in the 1830s : *'The village...is situated on the eastern bank of the Slaney, over which is a neat stone bridge. It has a penny post from Ferns, and is a constabulary police station'*.

Erected around 1780, this is a typical eighteenth century Irish road bridge. The seven main arches, flanked by smaller arches, orm an elegant yet functional structure. The arches are formed of the usual cut stone voissoirs, divided from one another by thin shale inserts. Two small flood arches formed of schist fieldstone have been propped up at their centres to withstand heavy traffic loads. The pointed cutwaters are taken up to parapet level to act as pedestrian refuges. Although the bridge is likely to have been founded on rock where it lies near the surface in this area, there will have been movement within the structure, in particular in the fill between the spandrel walls. Traffic loading results, in time, in a tendency for the spandrel walls to bulge outwards. In the case of the central arch, this has been counteracted by inserting tie bars through the fill and securing them to so-called 'pattress' plates abutting the vertical faces of the walls. In order to minimize the leaching of the mortar from the joints in the undersides (soffits) of the arches, concrete has been sprayed on to the surface. Concrete protective skirts have also been provided around the bases of the bridge's piers.

When the arches were being erected, temporary timber centering would have been provided to support the arch rings during erection. This timber framework was supported on stone brackets projecting from the piers at the springing level (bottom) of each arch. Such brackets often remain after the centering has been removed, as can be seen today under the arches of Ballycarney Bridge.

SCARAWALSH (1790) (bridge no.25)

Scairbh a' Bhreathnaigh, Walsh's scarriff. When a river spread widely over a craggy or rugged spot, the rough shallow ford thus formed was often called a scairbh.

Nearby is the townland of Tincurry, birthplace of 1798 hero, Father John Murphy. The first outbreak of the '98 rebellion in County Wexford occurred at Tincurry on the 26th May when the Piper household was raided for arms.

On Moll's map of 1714, a ferry service is indicated at this place.

An old wooden bridge at Scarawalsh was swept away by floods in 1787. The present masonry arch bridge was built in 1790 by the two Oriel brothers from Hampshire, England, who, in 1775, built Enniscorthy bridge.

The bridge connects what is now the N80 Bunclody to Enniscorthy road with the road to Ballycarney on the east bank of the river. Travellers from Dublin would also have crossed here. In 1976, the bridge was bypassed.

The six segmental arches increase in span from 21ft 6in near the banks to 32ft 6in over the main waterway, thus giving the bridge a hump back. The overall length of the bridge is around 310ft. and each of the approach embankments are around 70ft in length. The arch rings are formed of roughly-cut stones and the spandrel walls of even rougher 'fieldstone'. An excellent example of a late eighteenth century 'rural' road bridge, built to a generous width of 21ft and never widened or altered in any other way.

SCARAWALSH (1976) (bridge no.26)

This bridge, which opened in 1976, replaced the old (1790) masonry bridge at Scarawalsh which previously carried the road from Dublin to Wexford across the River Slaney.

The N11 (Euroroute 01) is carried over the Slaney at Scarawalsh by a 128ft span reinforced concrete box girder bridge.
The deck is an integral part of the box, the whole being cast in-situ and post-tensioned after the concrete was allowed harden and come up to full strength. The bridge rests on neoprene bearings on reinforced concrete abutments, the bearings allowing the bridge to move under the influence of temperature changes and other environmental effect.
The bridge was designed by McCarthy & Partners under the supervision of Professor Swako of Liverpool University. The contractors were Public Works Limited. The structural engineer, Peter Sheehy, worked on the design of the substructure of the bridge at Scarawalsh and later went on to design the concrete bridges at Ferrycarrig, Enniscorthy and Wexford for John B. Barry & Partners.

ENNISCORTHY RAIL (bridge no.27)

In 1860, counties Mayo, Leitrim, Sligo and Wexford were still not served by railway.

The Bagenalstown & Wexford Railway, operated by the GS&WR, sought to reach the sea-port of Wexford through Ballywilliam. The Borris-Ballywilliam section opened on 17th March 1862, but the company went bankrupt later in the year.

In 1860, the D&WR changed its title to the Dublin, Wicklow & Wexford Railway. Construction was slow from Wicklow to Arklow and it took almost two years to reach Avoca.

The section to Enniscorthy opened on 16th November 1863. This remained the end of the line for a further nine years.

On 17th August 1872, the DW&WR reached Wexford town. The building of the Enniscorthy to Wexford section included the construction of a rail bridge across the Slaney at Enniscorthy, a rail tunnel under the town and the present Enniscorthy railway station.

The rail crossing at Enniscorthy is the only railway bridge on the River Slaney today.

The rails are conveyed across the river on a short viaduct of seven spans [steel girders on masonry piers with latticed railings).

This was not the only rail bridge across the Slaney. In 1886, the GSWR built a branch line from Sallins to Tullow which crossed the Slaney a few miles to the south of Baltinglass on the border between counties Wicklow and Carlow. The branch was closed in 1959 and the iron bridge removed. The masonry abutments probably still survive but are inaccessible.

ENNISCORTHY (bridge no. 28)

Inis Córthaigh. Inis, an island; *'Córthaigh',* an ancient tribe?

This place was granted to Basilea, sister of Strongbow, on her marriage to Raymond Le Gros. The castle, which was built by Philip de Prendergast, was later owned by the McMurroughs and was subsequently granted to the Franciscan Order. The lands were later assigned to Sir Henry Wallop, ancestor of the Earl of Portsmouth. He exploited the area's vast timber resources.

Mr. P.J. Roche had business concerns in New Ross and Enniscorthy from about 1853 until his death in 1905. He purchased the castle which was in ruins and had it restored. When the castle was for sale in 1961, Father Joseph Ranson, a local historian, successfully campaigned for its purchase and conversion to a museum.

In the rebellion of 1798, the town was attacked and taken by rebels. Loyalists fled and the rebels set up camp on nearby Vinegar Hill. On the morning of June 21st, the camp was attacked by Crown Forces numbering about 15,000 troops. The Battle of Vinegar Hill ensued, with some of the heaviest fighting taking place on Enniscorthy Bridge. The rebels were ultimately forced to flee and, suffering heavy losses, they retreated to Wexford town. The story of '98 can be seen today in Enniscorty at the National 1798 Centre and the town museum.

The town square has a '98 monument by Oliver Sheppard, erected shortly after the success of his pikeman statue in Wexford.

St. Aidan's cathedral in Enniscorthy was built in the 1840s to the design of A.W. Pugin, the famous English architect.

At the end of the tidal stretch on the River Slaney, goods were shipped from Enniscorthy to Wexford town for export and imports were brought back on the rising tide in flat-bottomed cots (Irish *Coite*, a log-boat). This business declined with the arrival of the railways.

The town's water supply was installed in 1712 and in 1796, Enniscorthy had 23 registered malthouses, reflecting the importance of the grain trade in the area. The quays were built in the 1830s at a cost of £9,000. The Jameson distillery was established in 1815 at The Still. Marconi, inventor of the wireless, was the son of Annie Jameson of The Still.

ENNISCORTHY BRIDGE

One of the few early mentions of bridges in County Wexford is a contract drawn up by Lord Deputy Grey for the construction of a timber bridge at Enniscorthy, in 1581. It is unknown if it ever was built. A diagram of it shows a central castle tower of stone with a draw-bridge on each side.

An account exists of a bridge at Enniscorthy in 1680 which was destroyed in a flood.

A stone bridge was built here in 1775 by the Oriel brothers of Hampshire, England. (They also built Scarawalsh bridge).

In 1837, the Grand Jury of County Wexford and the ground landlords of Enniscorthy, the Portsmouth Estate, jointly paid for the widening and reconstruction of this bridge which included a further arch on the west bank.

An ancient crossing on the River Slaney at the end of the tidal stretch, Enniscorthy bridge linked Templeshannon with the commercial area of Enniscorthy that grew in the early 19th century.

The 1775 bridge of four masonry arches replaced an earlier seventeenth century structure. In the 1837 works, road improvements were introduced to ease the approach of traffic to the bridge. The arch rings are formed from thin flat schist stones. The present rounded cutwaters (downstream) with hemispherical tops are more typical of nineteenth century masonry bridges, so were probably replacements during the reconstruction. The upper side retains the original pointed cutwaters.

SÉAMUS RAFTER (bridge no.29)

This new bridge bears a plaque: 'Wexford County Council, Séamus Rafter Bridge. Opened by Padraic Flynn T.D., Minister of the Environment, on the 31st May 1991. Consulting engineers John B. Barry and Partners. Contractors Ascon Limited'.

At the bridge there is a statue to Séamus Rafter, 'Comdt. Of the Irish Volunteers 1916'. He had a provisions business at 'The Cotton Tree', Enniscorthy, and he died following an explosion there in 1918. He is buried at his native Ballindaggin. His memorial statue was erected at Abbey Square in 1958 and was moved to its present location in 1990.

This modern road bridge in the centre of Enniscorthy was built to solve the traffic problem in the town by creating (with the old bridge) a one-way system. The flat reinforced concrete beams spanning between the abutments and the piers have been disguised to resemble low-rise arches in order to be more aesthetically acceptable. The central span is 68ft and the two side spans each 50ft. Vertical detailing on the surface of the concrete also adds to the overall pleasing effect. Séamus Rafter Bridge is of in-situ reinforced concrete construction. It is a solid slab with fully integral piers and bearings on abutments supported on piles on the west side and on a wall sitting on bedrock on the east side.

EDERMINE (bridge no.30)

Eadarmhaighean - appears to be a late development (16th century) from *Eadardhroim*, 'central place'.

In the 1830s, Samuel Lewis wrote : *'A parish of 4,015 acres, with 213 inhabitants, on the mail coach road from Wexford to Dublin. The gentlemen's seats are Edermine, residence of Laurence Toole, Esq., and Rochfort, residence of J. Jervis Emerson, Esq.'*

Edermine was the Wexford home and farm of the Power's, distillers of whiskey, who resided at Portmarnock, County Dublin. They built a terrace of houses for their workers in the nearby village of Oilgate.

The first meeting of the Society of Friends (Quakers) in County Wexford took place at Edermine in 1657. The Quaker movement, like other religious sects, emerged from the turmoil in England in the 1600s. Many Cromwellian soldiers joined the Quakers and there were over 70 meeting houses in Ireland in 1670, with Cork, Clonmel and Waterford becoming important Quaker centres.

Edermine Bridge is also called *Marmion Bridge* after Don Columba Marmion, Abbot of the Benedictine monks of Maredsous in Belgium, who took refuge in Edermine House during World War 1.

Edermine is the only single-lane bridge on the Slaney. It replaced an earlier bridge, constructed of wood and metal in1898, which became weak with the arrival of heavy vehicles. By the 1960s it was only fit for use by pedestrians and cyclists.

The opening ceremony of the new Edermine bridge was performed in August 1975 by Wexford hurling star Nicky Rackard.

The old bridge of 1898 provided access from the main Enniscorthy-Wexford road (now the N11) to the dense network of county roads serving the farming communities to the west of the Slaney and to Macmine Junction from where trains ran to New Ross and Waterford. This bridge was replaced in reinforced concrete in 1974/5, the contractor being IrishEngCo. The concrete deck spans between transverse beams are supported at intervals by pairs of spiral reinforced concrete piles driven into the river-bed. These slender piles are raked at an angle to withstand the force of the flow of water in the river.

DEEPS (KILLURIN) (bridge no.31)

Cill Liúrain, St. Liurain's church.

The traveller Samuel Lewis wrote in the 1830s: *'Seats are Killurin House, lately the residence of the Devereux family, now the property of the Earl of Arran; Healthfield, of E. Beatty, Esq., and Penzance, of C. Martin, Esq.'*

After the Cromwellian campaign, the manor of the Deeps became the property of the Randalls who were associated with the establishment of the Society of Friends, (Quakers). Their first meeting in County Wexford was at Edermine in 1657.

This 1915 bridge crosses the Slaney at a point called The Deeps. Nearby are the ruins of the Deeps castle, situated at a stretch of the Slaney which is particularly deep.

The present bridge replaced a timber trestle bridge erected in 1842-44 under the direction of the County Surveyor, James Barry Farrell. Deeps bridge consists, on the eastern side of the river, of five spans, each of 30ft, approached by a 216ft long embankment terminating in a masonry abutment.

On the western side of the waterway there are five spans, four of 30ft and one of 19ft 6in. Between these spans there is a bascule-type steel lifting span of 40ft opening to maintain the navigation, placed between two fixed sections. The supporting piers consist of reinforced concrete pile groups carried up to the deck and cross-braced. The overall length of the bridge is around 610ft, some 360ft of that being over the waterway. The carriageway is just over 18ft wide.The bridge was designed by the Dublin consulting firm of Delap and Waller and erected in 1915 by the British Reinforced Concrete Engineering Company, using BRC Fabric as the reinforcement. A contemporary company advertisement described this fabric as 'a continuous wire mesh of drawn steel wires laid in the concrete along the lines where the tension is greatest, each wire taking its share of the work'. The lifting span was supplied by the Cleveland Engineering Company.

FERRYCARRIG (bridge no.32)

Faradh na Carraige, the Ferry of Carrig (*carraig*, rock).

Before 1795 there was no bridge across the River Slaney below Enniscorthy and ferry services operated at Scarawalsh, Ferrycarrig and Wexford town. The 15th century tower house at Ferrycarrig was built by the Roches to guard the ferry.

The site of Fitz-Stephen's castle at Ferrycarrig has a round tower monument commemorating men from Wexford who were killed in the Crimea war. It was built by local architect, Thomas Willis, in 1858. Nearby is the Irish National Heritage Park, which opened in 1987.

The American engineer, Lemuel Cox, constructed a toll bridge here of American oak in 1795. The proposed bridge was first discussed at a meeting in the New Hotel, Wexford town, in January of that year. The meeting was chaired by Cornelius Grogan of Johnstown Castle who, ironically, was hanged at another bridge of Lemuel Cox's three years later at Wexford, in the rebellion year of 1798.

Cox's oak bridge was replaced in 1912 by a concrete bridge built by Robert Colhoun of Derry, at a cost of £5,290. That bridge lasted until 1980 and was then replaced. A section of it remains beside the new modern bridge. Remains of the 1795 timber bridge may also be seen upstream.

The replacement bridge of 1912 used reinforced concrete and the bridge was designed to the French Hennibique system by Mouchel & Partners of London. From 1972, loads on the bridge were limited to 3 tons and it was restricted to cars only. The present bridge (1980) was designed by John B. Barry & Partners and erected by ASCON.

It spans 410ft (125m). The seven river piers at 51ft 6in centres are formed of steel tubular piles driven down to rock and encased at their upper levels in concrete. The piers support a deck comprised of pre-cast pre-stressed concrete inverted T-beams forming a continuous superstructure.

WEXFORD (bridge no.33)

Weisford, ford of the mud flats. Also called *Loch Garman*.

A monastic site at Begerin was plundered by the Vikings who arrived in 819. They conducted destructive raids inland from their base at *Weisford*.

The Normans came in 1169. They expanded the town and built a castle and defensive stone wall. In 1649, Cromwell captured Ferns, Enniscorthy and Wexford town.

The Bullring contains a 1798 pikeman statue by Oliver Sheppard which was unveiled in 1905. The rebellion of 1798 greatly affected the town and one of the worst atrocities of the rebellion happened at Wexford bridge on 20th June, 1798. Loyalist prisoners were taken from their cells and went through a hasty 'courts martial' headed by rebel captain, Thomas Dixon. Sentenced

to death, the prisoners were made to kneel down whereupon they were 'piked' by their executioners, held up in the air on pikes and thrown over the bridge parapet into the tide. Over 90 are thought to have been killed. Dixon later disappeared.After the rebellion, many rebel leaders were hanged on the bridge, including the main bridge shareholder, Cornelius Grogan, of Johnstown Castle. Dixon, the culprit most deserving of retribution, escaped and was never heard of again.

Wexford dockyard opened in 1832, a year that also saw the opening of the Theatre Royal in High Street where, today, the international Wexford Opera Festival attracts patrons each autumn. The Opera Festival started in 1951.

In 1839, Pierce's foundry began making fire fans and, in 1866, the company was employed in the construction of a bridge across the River Slaney at Wexford.

Work began on the twin churches in 1851 and the project took seven years to complete. Saint Peter's College, which opened in 1819, contains an architecturally important chapel built to the design of A.W. Pugin, (architect of Enniscorthy cathedral).

The railway reached Wexford from Enniscorthy in 1872, adding further to the town's prosperity. Wexford port shipped goods to many countries and in the early 1900s, Wexford manufacturers of agricultural machinery had offices in Paris and Buenos Aires.

WEXFORD BRIDGE

A ferry service across the Slaney was replaced by the building of a bridge in 1795, by Lemuel Cox, which was constructed of American oak.

His bridge at Wexford took nine months to build and cost £15,000. It was 1,554 ft long and 34 ft wide and was a toll bridge until 1851. A portion of it had a drawbridge to facilitate ships. Regimental music was performed on fine days in balconies constructed on the bridge.

A new bridge was built in 1866 further upriver by Philip Pierce and Company, of Wexford. The bridge was designed by Thomas Willis, to the plans of James Barry Farrell, County Surveyor, which lasted until 1959.

The new bridge of 1959 was a seven-span pre-stressed cantilevered concrete structure, 1256ft in length, built near the site of the original timber bridge by ASCON to the design of a Dutchman, Dr H.C.Duyster working with O'Connell & Harley of Cork. It was a major civil engineering achievement. Pre-stressed concrete had never before been used in such a large project in Ireland and it marked the formation of the contracting firm of ASCON.

During the 1980s, after some twenty years in a marine environment, the bridge began to show signs of deterioration of the concrete and corrosion of the reinforcement, due largely to the action of chloride ions in the concrete, a process that was then only beginning to be fully understood. Thus, in September/November, 1997, the bridge was demolished down to the tops of the piers and a new superstructure provided, consisting of continuous steel plate girders with a composite reinforced concrete deck slab. The girders were supplied and erected by an Italian company, Construzioni Cimolai Armando SpA. The project was completed by ASCON in less than ten weeks of bridge closure and the bridge was reopened to the public on 22 November 1997. The structural consultants were John B.Barry & Partners. The bridge won a Construction Excellence Award in 1998.

Chapter 6

Fishing and Boating on the River Slaney

FISHING ON THE RIVER SLANEY

The Slaney abounds with trout and salmon :
entry in Ordnance field books, 1839.

Presently at an all-time low in the history
of angling, the River Slaney, which once had
an international reputation, is now a shadow
of its former self. It is beset with many problems and there are as many theories of problem and solution as there are fishing tales.

Of primary concern is the plight of salmon
stocks throughout the river system. Salmon
return annually from the sea to the streams
in which they were born, then mate and lay
their eggs in 'redds' (beds of stone & gravel
in shallow well-oxygenated water). Surviving parr migrate downriver to the sea where
rich feeding means rapid body growth and,
after a few years, they return to their place
of birth to spawn.

Factors blamed for declining stocks include
river pollution, global warming, predators
(including anglers) and the netting of salmon
returning to spawn.

Redd (spawning bed) counts on the River Slaney System 1995 – 2005

Main Slaney	1995	1996	1997	1998	1999	2000	2001	2002	2003	2004	2005
Various bridges											
Ford-Seskin	8	6	-	12	24	8	0	20	H.W	-	29
Seskin-Ballinclea	103	84	71	110	122	48	57	88	39	15	61
Ballinclea-Kelsha	87	15	19	111	98	48	54	113	39	13	31
Kelsha-Gibstown	53	19	11	50	68	13	29	46	18	7	5
Gibstown-Knockaderry	-	-	8	-	19	7	0	61	H.W.	4	0
K'derry-Ballyhubbock	80	38	52	52	34	43	43	61	26	15	11
B'hubbock-George's	56	21	27	73	38	12	15	30	H.W.	5	11
George's-Waterloo	-	20	9	5	8	6	0	7	H.W.	1	2
Waterloo-Stratford	-	13	6	11	14	9	0	21	H.W.	2	0
Stratford-Manger	80	128	84	108	98	18	20	25	H.W.	7	12
Manger-Tuckmill	26	100	28	67	81	49	28	4	56	11	0
Tuckmill-Eldon	54	34	27	39	66	37	43	105	H.W.	7	34
Eldon-Baltinglass	35	-	-	24	32	17	75	10	H.W.	4	0
B'glass-Aldborough	72	212	189	80	186	143	H.W.19	155	H.W.	62	82
Total main channel	690	531	742	888	458	383	746	H.W	165	278	435
Total tributaries	564	837	361	575	412	314	837	H.W	170	452	563
Total Slaney System	1254	1368	1103	1463	870	697	1583	H.W	335	730	998

Working from Source downstream   H.W. denotes High Water   Figures supplied by Eastern Regional Fisheries Board

ROD FISHING

'Although the best and largest Trouts bite in the Night (being afraid to stir, or range about in the Daytime) yet I account this way of Angling both unwholesome, unpleasant and very ungentiel, and to be used only by none but Idle pouching Fellows'.

James Chetham, *The Angler's Vade-Mecum* (1681)

Fishing rights on the River Slaney are owned by private landowners and the Eastern Regional Fisheries Board who rent out fishing to individuals and angling clubs for the fishing season. (Fishing is free in the tidal stretch below Enniscorthy). The season is from March to September and prime fishing time for salmon is from opening date to June.

There are many fishing beats between Tullow and Enniscorthy but the most favoured fly-fishing pools are below Bunclody. Above Tullow, fly-fishing conditions are more difficult as the river is small and the banks are overgrown.

Rod catches of salmon on the River Slaney between 1927 and 1963 were up to 2,500 per annum. The current rod catch is estimated to be as low as 508 in 2004 and 364 in 2005. Many fish in the past were over 20 lbs. but nowadays the average weight is 10 lbs. or lower. Nevertheless, the odd surprise occurs such as at Scarawalsh in the early 90s, when a 35 pounder and a 20 pounder were caught on one day, from one pool.

Drift netting at sea (to end in 2006?) is blamed for intercepting a lot of returning salmon but graphs also show that stocks never recovered from UDN disease in the 1960s. Catches per rod licence in the Wexford District were 12.9 in 1964 and 0.63 in 2004. There are four times more anglers on the River Slaney now than in the 1960s and back then, fishing was only allowed between the hours of 10a.m. and 5p.m.

The River Slaney has a sizeable run of sea trout each summer, whose life cycle mirrors that of their larger cousins. Their average weight might be less than 2lbs. but they are prized for their fighting spirit. Native brown trout are plentiful, though small. The best brown trout fishing is considered to be in the upper half of the river. Their average size is less than 1lb. but, like salmon, surprises also occur. In 2001, this author caught a brown trout at Tullow that weighed 4lbs.10oz . Another surprise occurred in the 1890s when a 7ft. sturgeon was taken from the River Slaney at Scarawalsh.

Kingsmill Moore, Kilcarry, author of *'A man may fish'* (1960)

DRAFT (estuary) NET FISHING

Declining salmon stocks are reflected in estuary net catches today. In the 1960s, before UDN disease, the average catch per net was close to 50 salmon per year but nowadays the figure is about 15.

The number of net licences on 13 miles of the Slaney estuary is 75 (including 5 on the coast) and the annual allowable catch is 1,130 salmon. Despite a reduction of about 50% in the numbers caught by nets since the shortening of their season from 1996 onwards, increased fish numbers have not been seen in the river. The present net season is from 12th May to 12th August and netsmen no longer have the peak month of April. Netting is confined to 4 days a week and not allowed within a mile of tributaries entering the Slaney.

In the 1960s, fish buyers supplied netsmen with a boat, net and licence. Licences were handed down through the years in netsmens' families.

Early nets were of tarred cotton but today, nylon is used. (Monofilament was banned in the 1960s.) Nets today measure 72 fathoms by 9 feet and netting is a 2 man job where one rows out and the other remains on the bank. The operation takes about 20 minutes.

The average annual nets catch between 2001 and 2004 was 980 salmon and 2000 sea trout. Small sea trout manage to get through the 3.5in. mesh.

In the 1960s, good prices obtained for wild salmon but nowadays, faced by competition from farmed salmon and, facing dwindling stocks, the economics of the practice comes into question.

'...the trout or salmon, being in season, have their bodies adorned, the one with such red spots, and the other such black or blackish spots, as give them such an addition of natural beauty, as I think was never given to any woman by the artificial paint or patches in which they so much pride themselves in this age'.

Izaak Walton, *The Compleat Angler*, (1653)

THE EASTERN REGIONAL FISHERIES BOARD

THE SLANEY RIVER TRUST LTD.

The ERFB was established in 1980. Part of its function is to protect, conserve and promote inland fisheries. The Wexford District of the ERFB covers from Wicklow Head to Kilmore Quay and inland to the Baltinglass area.

Prior to 1980, a Board of Conservators consisting of sixteen local fishery owners such as Brigadier Booth, Captain Lang, Commander Skrine and Captain Norton managed the Slaney fishery. (These Boards went back to 1860.) Also on the Board were four netsmen from the river.

The ERFB controls 8 km. of angling water, at Tullow and Kildavin. The Board also has a sea trout fishery on the river Boro. An 8 km. stretch of the river Bann below Ferns has been developed by the Board and a new angling club was formed in that area.

Poaching occurs in the Autumn in the Glen of Imaal, Donard, Rathvilly and Hacketstown areas, mainly at night. Salmon, having made it home to their spawning beds, are tired after their long journey from the sea and are easy prey to the poachers who catch them by net and by fork in the shallow pools, often just for sport. Fishery Board officers patrol these areas and are assisted by the Army in the Glen who have constructed an observation tower for this purpose.

In conjunction with the Slaney River Trust Ltd., the ERFB has conducted recent habitat improvements in spawning areas by constructing weirs and placing more than 300 tons of boulders and gravel along the Carrigower river near Donard and in the Derreen above Hacketstown.

The Slaney River Trust was established in 2004 with E.U., national and local funding and is dedicated to promoting the ecological welfare and development of the Slaney river system. Formed as a joint project with the Pembrokeshire River Trust in Wales, in an INTERREG project, it comprises the Central (and Eastern) Regional Fisheries Boards, South East Regional Tourism Authority, Trinity College, Dublin (Zoology Dept.), as well as being supported by individuals and angling clubs along the river.

Its main aim is to reverse the decline of salmon stocks and the Trust, working with the ERFB, has conducted habitat improvement works on the spawning areas of the Derreen, Derry and Carrigower rivers, and plan further projects into the future.

THE INLAND WATERWAYS ASSOCIATION OF IRELAND

The IWAI was founded in 1954 by enthusiasts keen to promote the use and development of Ireland's navigable rivers and canals. When the River Shannon was undeveloped for boating, the IWAI fought against the building of low bridges and thus helped preserve the River Shannon as an asset for the nation. The IWAI also successfully fought the threatened closure of the Grand Canal in Dublin and helped instigate the development of the River Barrow for boating. The IWAI has worked towards the restoration of the Royal Canal, the Ulster Canal and other closed navigations.

The Slaney branch of the IWAI was established to promote the use of the Slaney river navigation from Wexford up to Enniscorthy.

The key person behind the development of pleasure boating on the lower Slaney was Cecil Miller. Before the founding of the Slaney branch of the IWAI at Wexford in 1989, Cecil, assisted by Wexford Sea Scouts and others, produced the 'Slaney Guide' with navigational charts and notes on wildlife and history of the lower River Slaney.

Cecil Miller

Slaney Branch IWAI have landing sites at Ferrycarrig, Killurin, Edermine and Enniscorthy. The River Slaney is tidal from Wexford to Enniscorthy and boats with a draught of up to three feet can operate in this stretch. The Branch holds an annual rally and attends many waterways events throughout Ireland each year.

WEXFORD HARBOUR BOAT CLUB

Wexford Harbour Boat Club was founded in 1873 at a meeting held in White's Hotel, Wexford.

A boat house was built at a cost of £80 at Ferrybank. In 1874, the house and most of the boats were destroyed in a storm. On the opposite bank, new premises were built on land acquired from the Railway Company.

The Boat Club began its life as a rowing club and won many competitions in the early years. At the Wexford Harbour Regatta in 1873, the first race for out-rigged fours was won by Wexford competing against the Slaney Rowing Club of Enniscorthy.

GIRL CLAIRE

Sailing craft are thought to have arrived in the mid 1920s. Wexford Sailing Club was formed in 1945 and members took part in sailing races during the 50s and 60s.

Today, the Club continues to operate from the site acquired in the 1870s and has much expanded over the years. The game of tennis has been played at Club grounds since 1883 and, in 1994, tennis and boating were integrated when the Club's name officially became the Wexford Harbour Boat and Tennis Club.

ROWING and CANOEING
The sport of rowing on the River Slaney continues today and there are rowing clubs at Edermine, Killurin and Ferrycarrig. Rowing races are held on the river in July and August each year.

The main centres for canoeing on the River Slaney are at Tullow and Baltinglass, on the upper stretches of the river. The Outdoor Education Centre in Baltinglass, established in 1987, is funded by the Department of Education & Science and is managed by the VEC. It provides accommodation and students can take part in canoeing, hill walking, rock climbing, and other pursuits.

Boating on the River
Slaney

Chapter 7   Slaney Men of '98

Background to Rebellion
Michael Dwyer of Imaal
Father John Murphy of Boolavogue
Aftermath of Rebellion

BACKGROUND TO REBELLION

The United Irishmen Rebellion of 1798 was one of the biggest (and bloodiest) events in the history of Ireland with some 30,000 killed in the summer of that year. The southeast was where most conflict took place. The Slaney Valley suffered greatly and violent events occurred all along the river's course from the Glen of Imaal to Wexford town.

Influenced by the French Revolution and the War of Independence in America, the Society of United Irishmen was founded in Belfast in 1791 to seek political change. Some reform was allowed in1793 but this was 'too little, too late' as social conditions remained severe and Catholics could not be Members of Parliament or hold positions of authority in society.

A military force, from England's old enemy France, sailed to Ireland in December 1796 to assist the United Irishmen in rebellion. Arriving at Bantry Bay, County Cork, the 43 ships, containing 15,000 troops, were met with ferocious storms and were forced to return to France.

The Leinster leadership was arrested in March 1798 in Dublin and, shortly afterwards, United leader Lord Edward Fitzgerald was also captured in Dublin. Papers in his possession showed that there were 279,896 sworn United Irishmen across Ireland.

On the night of 23rd May, the rebellion began in Prosperous, County Kildare, where 50 militia were killed in an attack on a police station. The next day, an attack on Naas, County Kildare, failed with over 200 rebels killed. The day after that, soldiers in Carlow town waited in ambush and, when the rebels entered Tullow Street, 640 of them were killed.

In County Wicklow on 24th May, the day Stratford-on-Slaney was attacked, 36 prisoners in Dunlavin jail were taken to the village green and shot. The next day, 28 prisoners were shot dead in the ball alley at Carnew.

News of these atrocities spread quickly and the Rebellion would soon erupt in County Wexford.

Statue of a pikeman at The Bullring, Wexford.

MICHAEL DWYER OF IMAAL

Michael Dwyer was born in the townland of Camara, Glen of Imaal, in 1772. He was the eldest of seven children. The family had a small farm on the banks of the River Slaney, a short distance above where Seskin bridge now stands. When Michael Dwyer was 12, the family moved to Eadstown, four miles away, to a larger holding.

Prior to the rebellion, there were 14,000 United members in County Wicklow. Micheal Dwyer joined the Society of United Irishmen in 1797.

On the 24th May 1798, 36 prisoners (including a relation of Michael Dwyer's father) were shot on Dunlavin Green. This had a profound effect on Dwyer who was then 26 years of age. In the following years, Michael Dwyer and about 30 followers conducted a campaign against Government and local Yeomen militia throughout west Wicklow. They endured harsh conditions living in safe houses, caves and dugouts across the mountains in all weathers.

Dwyer took part in battles at Hacketstown, Arklow, Bunclody and Vinegar Hill, after which he returned to the security of the Wicklow mountains.

His most famous escape was from a cottage at Derrynamuck, Glen of Imaal, on the night of 15th February, 1799. As Dwyer and his followers slept in three safe houses, an informer went to the barracks in Hacket-

stown and betrayed them. Some hours later, the cottage containing Dwyer was surrounded by the Glengarry Fencibles.

The cottage was soon in flames and as the wounded Sam McAllister bravely went to the door and drew fire upon himself, Dwyer ran past the soldiers, bare-footed and half-dressed. He slipped on ice as musket balls flew over his head. A short distance away he jumped the flooded Little Slaney and the pursuing soldiers did not attempt to cross the torrent.

Of his eleven companions that night, three were killed and eight were captured. One of these turned informer and the other seven were executed at Baltinglass.

Five years after the ending of the rebellion, Dwyer's following had diminished, there was £500 on his head and the Government offered him 'a retreat from the Kingdom with all his family and several of his relations'.

Michael Dwyer surrendered to Mr. William Hoare Hume, M.P., at the Three Bridges, rear of Humewood Estate, Kiltegan, on 14th December, 1803. He believed he was to be pardoned and given safe passage with his family and some followers to the United States of America. Instead, he was placed in Kilmainham Jail for two years. He was then transported to New South Wales, Australia, accompanied by his wife, Mary Doyle of Knockandarragh, (near Donard), two of their four children, and five of his close followers. They went, not as convicts, but as 'free settlers'.

The career of Michael Dwyer was as colourful in Australia as his exploits in the Wicklow mountains. He became a farmer, policeman and publican, and his fondness for drink got worse. Governor William Bligh (of *Mutiny on the Bounty* fame) had him shipped for a time to Norfolk Island, a penal colony 800 miles out in the Pacific Ocean.

When the Dwyers sailed from Ireland they brought two daughters with them and left two sons behind. In Australia, they had a further son and two daughters. Michael Dwyer died on 23rd August 1825, at the age of 53. His wife, Mary, survived until 1861. Their two sons arrived from Ireland in 1828 to join their mother.

Michael and Mary Dwyer are buried in Waverley Cemetery, Sidney, where a large monument commemorates his name and that of other Irish rebels.

Statue of Micheal Dwyer
at Seskin

FATHER JOHN MURPHY OF BOOLAVOGUE

John Murphy, born in 1753, was one of five children born to Thomas Murphy and Johanna Whitty in the townland of Tincurry, near Scarawalsh bridge on the River Slaney, where his father was a tenant farmer and bacon curer.

In 1779, John Murphy was ordained by Bishop Nicholas Sweetman in Wexford. He studied in Seville, Spain, and returned home in 1785 to take up a post at Boolavogue, near his home.

In the lead up to the rebellion, the people had been encouraged to surrender their arms to gain 'protections' but, seeing that these were of little value and, after learning of atrocities in neighbouring counties, the priest joined with his flock in revolt.

On the 26th May 1798, a group led by Father Murphy encountered a cavalry patrol near The Harrow and in the skirmish that followed, Lieutenant Thomas Bookey and his deputy were killed. The rebellion in Wexford had begun.

Father Murphy's group quickly expanded and there were about 4,000 people with him on Oulart Hill on 27th May when the military attacked. The North Cork Militia suffered serious defeat that day. Out of 110 soldiers, only 5 escaped alive. The next day, Father Murphy and his followers captured Enniscorthy and soon after, rebels entered the deserted towns of Wexford and Gorey.

There were victories at Tubberneering and Ballyellis, but serious defeat was encountered at Arklow, Bunclody and New Ross. Failure to extend the rebellion beyond these towns meant that the rebellion was effectively 'pinned down' in County Wexford and after the rebels' defeat at Vinegar Hill, Enniscorthy, on 21st June, their fate was sealed.

Leaving Vinegar Hill, (where his brother was killed), Father Murphy led his followers through south County Carlow, going on to attack Castlecomer in County Kilkenny. Failing to find support, the group re-entered County Carlow and, following defeat at the Battle of Kilcumney, near Goresbridge, many were separated from the main group, including Father Murphy and his companion, James Gallagher of Tomahurra.

It is unknown why the two men headed northwards through east County Carlow. On 2nd July, they were arrested by a yeoman patrol on a farm at Castlemore, near Tullow, and taken to the town square where they were tortured and hanged.

Body parts were burned in a barrel and their remains are believed to be buried in the Mullawn graveyard, Tullow, on the banks of the River Slaney.

AFTERMATH OF REBELLION

A few months after it began, the 1798 Rebellion of the United Irishmen was over. About 30,000 people, including some 7,000 soldiers, died that year.

Rebels were hunted down and killed and United leaders were rounded up and executed, (many of them on Wexford bridge). Large numbers were transported to Australia or forced into the British army and navy. More joined armies on the Continent where some had distinguished military careers.

The Irish Parliament was abolished and the Act of Union was passed in 1800. Parliament buildings in College Green, Dublin, were sold to a commercial bank and Catholic Emancipation was not granted until 1829.

The Dwyer/McAllister cottage in Derrynamuck, Glen of Imaal, became a National Monument in 1948 and An Taoiseach, Mr. Bertie Ahern, unveiled a statue to Michael Dwyer and his followers on 14th December, 2003, at Seskin, Glen of Imaal, on the 200th anniversary of Dwyer's surrender.

Today, there is the Dwyer Trail in Imaal and, in County Wexford, one can visit the Father Murphy Centre at Boolavogue and the National 1798 Centre in Enniscorthy. The museums in Enniscorthy and Tullow also have material from the '98 period.

At the rebellion's bicentenary in 1998, many parades took place featuring men and women dressed as pikemen of old. One of the largest gatherings was when a parade of 1,500 pikemen, led by the Boolavogue pike group, marched through the town of Tullow on the 5th July that year and assembled at the Father Murphy statue, in memory of the rebel priest.

Statue of Father Murphy at Tullow

A print illustration of the suffering in County Wicklow in 1798.
The print was published in the Christmas edition of the Irish Weekly Independent, December 1899.
The original painting is by Walter C. Mills.

Chapter 8   Slaney Miscellaneous

WEXFORD SEAFARING TRADITION

By the 10th century, Wexford was an established Viking port from where voyages went to Wales and as far off as the Bay of Biscay and northern Spain.

In the middle ages, large quantities of fish, especially herring, were exported, primarily to Wales, and boats returned with cargoes of Welsh coal. In 1598, Wexford and Waterford operated more ships than all other Irish ports combined. Timber, hides, and fish were exported and imports were wine, salt and iron. In the 1630s, Wexford annually exported 100,000 barrels of fish.

In 1837, there were 110 registered vessels at Wexford, manned by 690 sailors. They operated as far afield as the Black Sea, Turkey, Greece, West Africa and America. There was also substantial passenger traffic and, from 1822, paddle steamers began to operate out of Wexford. The Wexford Steamship Company, founded in 1930 by the Stafford family, played a large part in bringing supplies into Ireland during the second world war.

Eventually, the natural shallow harbour of Wexford could not handle bigger craft and centuries of seafaring tradition began to enter decline. Rosslare harbour opened in 1896 and in 1970 the Irish Government turned down the possibility of reviving Wexford port. Today, the harbour is much used by boating enthusiasts.

At The Crescent there is a statue to John Barry, native of Our Lady's Island, who is regarded as 'the Father of the American Navy'. The statue was presented by the United States of America to the town of Wexford in 1956.

WEXFORD WILDFOWL RESERVE

THE RIVER GODS OF EDWARD SMYTH

Jointly owned and managed by BirdWatch Ireland and Dúchas, the Sloblands in Wexford harbour are a world-famous nature reserve for migrating and over-wintering birds. 250 bird species have been recorded, the birds being attracted to the habitat of a wide shallow harbour with mudbanks and sandbars. Greylag geese from Iceland were first recorded here in 1898. About one third of the world population of Greenland White-fronted Geese visit the Slobs, as do many species of waders, ducks, swans and other birds.

Reclaimed from the shallow harbour, the Slobs are protected from the sea by large Dutch-like dykes and a pump house controls water levels within the Slobs. Visitors view the birds from the many 'hides' on the site.

In 1928, the artist Sir John Lavery was employed by the Currency Commission to paint a portrait emblematic of an Irish colleen for the front of Irish bank notes. The portrait depicts a seated woman, (believed to be Lady Lavery), her arm resting upon a harp and the background has lake and mountain scenery. The designs on the back of the notes, by portrait engraver Mr. John Harrison of London, are based on Edward Smyth's sculptures of the River God Heads on the Custom House, Dublin. Each denomination has a different head and relates to different Irish rivers, i.e. £100 – Erne; £50 - Shannon; £20 -Boyne; £10 - Bann; £5 - Lagan; £1 – Lee and 10/-, the Blackwater. (Though featured on the Custom House, the Slaney God was not used on currency notes).

Dublin's Custom House was designed by the English architect, James Gandon, and built in the 1780s at a cost of over £200,000. Gandon initially relied on the skills of English sculptors to decorate his buildings but

he discovered Edward Smyth in Dublin, an employee of his stone-cutting contractor. Edward Smyth (1749-1812) was born in County Meath, the son of a stone-cutter. He served an apprenticeship in Dublin to Simon Vierpyl, a Flemish sculptor. While a young man, Smyth won a major competition with his statue of Lord Lucas for the Royal Exchange, (now Dublin City Hall), but success did not readily follow and he was engaged in mundane projects for about 10 years until his introduction to Gandon, who quickly recognised his talent. He subsequently worked on all of Gandon's Irish buildings.

On Dublin's Custom House, Edward Smyth's depiction of the heads of 13 River Gods and the Atlantic Ocean form the keystones of the ground-floor arches. The heads each measure about 90cm x 30cm and are carved from Portland stone. The rivers depicted are: the Bann, Barrow, Blackwater, Boyne, Erne, Foyle, Lagan, Lee, Liffey, Nore, Shannon, Slaney and Suir. Each god head

Irish £20 note featuring Sir John Lavery's painting on front, and the River Boyne god head on rear.

contains symbolic representation of the produce of its area: the Blackwater Head has a
basket of apples and fish while the Lagan has
folds of linen, representing the linen industry
of Belfast. The Slaney Head has corn, oysters,
scallops and crabs.

The Liffey Head is the only female one.
She occupies a position over the main en-
trance facing onto the quays and the River
Liffey. This head is crowned by flowers &
fruit and features a trident representing
Dublin's powers over Dublin Bay and the
Irish Sea. Smyth produced other works for
the Custom House, including the Arms of
Ireland, showing the union of England,
Scotland and Ireland. He also produced the
statue at the Four Courts of Moses holding
the Tables of Law.

Slaney River God

SLANEY BRIDGE 'RECORDS'

Lemuel Cox's Wexford bridge, built of American oak in 1795. (Painting by H. Mitchell)

Number of Slaney bridges in 2006	33	First Slaney toll bridge	Ferrycarrig (1795)
First bridge	Seskin	Bridge that hosted a battle	Enniscorthy (Battle of Vinegar Hill in 1798)
Last bridge	Wexford	Longest Slaney bridge ever built	Wexford wooden bridge, 1795, (1554 ft.)
Oldest bridge	Manger	Bridge with recesses for two orchestras	Wexford wooden bridge, 1795
Newest bridge	Wexford	Bridge that hosted murders	Wexford wooden bridge in 1798
Shortest bridge	George's	Bridge on which its principal shareholder was hanged	Wexford wooden bridge in 1798
Longest bridge	Wexford	Bridge with stand-in pedestrian refuges	Ballycarney
Number of bridges on the Slaney in 1656	One	Bridge beside an artillery range	Seskin
Number of bridges above Baltinglass in 1760	Two	Widest single-span masonry bridge	Waterloo
Number of bridges below Enniscorthy in 1794	None	Bridge at end of tidal stretch	Enniscorthy

Only rail bridge	Enniscorthy	Most overgrown bridge	Tuckmill
Only single-lane bridge	Edermine	Most fished-off bridge	Enniscorthy
One-way bridges	Two (in Enniscorthy)	Most busy bridge	New Scarawalsh
Bridges faced entirely with cut granite	Moatabower and Tullow	Least busy bridge	Kelsha
Bridges in two counties	Kildavin and Bunclody	Most battered-by-vehicles bridge	Eldon
Last stone bridge	Enniscorthy	Strangest-looking bridge	Edermine
Award-winning bridge	Wexford (1998)	Non-public bridge	Army bridge, Glen of Imaal.
Bridge with navigational lifting section	Killurin	Most charming bridge (artist's opinion)	Old Scarawalsh
Number of bridges below Killurin with no lifting section	Two	Least charming bridge (artist's opinion)	Enniscorthy rail
Most impressive parapet stones	Bunclody	Bridge opened by uncle-in-law of artist	Edermine

BIBLIOGRAPHY

Barry, Michael, Across Deep Waters, Dublin, 1985

Cox, Ronald, and Gould, Michael, Ireland's Bridges, Dublin, 2003

Dickson, Charles, Life of Michael Dwyer, Dublin, 1944

Doyle, Oliver, and Hirsch, Stephen, Railways in Ireland, 1834-1984, Dublin, 1983

Furlong, Nicholas, Fr. John Murphy of Boolavogue 1753-1798, Dublin, 1991

Gahan, Daniel, The People's Rising, Dublin, 1995

Hannigan, Ken and Nolan,William, (editors), Wicklow: History and Society, Dublin, 1994

Healy, Elizabeth, The River Gods, Dublin 1998

Joyce, P.W., Irish Names of Places, Dublin, 1913

Lewis, Samuel, A Topographical Dictionary of Ireland, London, 1837

O'Donnell, Ruan, (editor), Insurgent Wicklow 1798, by Luke Cullen, Bray, 1998

O'Donovan, John, Ordnance Survey Field Books, 1839

O'Keeffe, Peter, and Simmington, Tom, Irish Stone Bridges, Dublin, 1991

O'Toole, Edward, Place Names of County Carlow, Carlow 1937

O'Toole, Jimmy, The Carlow Gentry, Carlow, 1993

Price, Liam, The Place Names of County Wicklow, Dublin, 1945

Rowe, D. and Wilson, C.J. (editors), High Skies – Low Lands, An Anthology of the Wexford Slobs and Harbour, Enniscorthy, 1996

Scallan, Eithne, The Boat Club, Wexford, 2004

Whelan, Kevin and Nolan, William, (editors), Wexford: History and Society, Dublin, 1992

BRIDGE GLOSSARY

ABUTMENT The body (usually river bank) that provides the resistance offered to the horizontal thrust of an arch.

ARCH A curved structure capable of carrying its own weight and additional loads.

ARCH RING Assembly of stones in a masonry arch – often referred to as 'voussoirs'.

ASHLAR Stones that have been carefully hewn and worked.

BALUSTRADE Railing supported by a series of short ornamental pillars.

BEAM A usually straight structure capable of spanning a gap.

BOX GIRDER A hollow girder, usually square or rectangular, used in modern-day bridge construction.

CUTWATER The protruding end of a bridge pier to divide flowing water and deflect floating objects.

EXTRADOS Convex surface of an arch.

FIELDSTONE Stone occurring locally on the ground surface.

FILL Gravel, earth or rubble used between retaining walls.

HENNIBIQUE SYSTEM A reinforcing system in concrete using steel.

INTRADOS Concave surface of an arch.

KEYSTONE The stone placed last at the top of an arch.

MASONRY Stonework or the work of a mason.

ORIEL Decorative circular feature in wall, usually over a pier.

PEDESTRIAN REFUGE 'Stand-in' area on top of extended cutwater.

PIER Pillar support between arches.

RUBBLE STONE Quarried stones of angular shape and random size.

RUSTICATED ASHLAR Hammer-dressed stone where the surface is left rough and stands out from the joints.

SEGMENTAL ARCH Arch of less than a semi-circle.

SOFFIT Underside of arch.

SPAN Distance between arch supports.

SPRANDREL WALL Wall area between two arches, below road level.

STRING COURSE Horizontal projecting stonework on wall face.

TIE BAR Metal rod binding bridge walls to prevent movement.

VOUSSOIRS Arch stones of tapered or wedge shape.

www.irish-rivers.com